USBORNE
THE GREAT WILDLIFE SEARCH

Caroline Young
Kate Needham
Illustrated by Ian Jackson

Designed by
Andy Dixon & Andy Griffin

Contents

The Great Undersea Search 1
The Big Bug Search 33
The Great Animal Search 65
Index 111

Series editor: Felicity Brooks

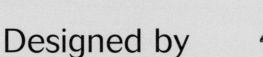

Managing Designer:	Mary Cartwright
Design Assistant:	Susannah Owen
Editor for *Big Bug Search*:	Kamini Khanduri
Editorial Assistants:	Rosie Heywood
	Rachel Swann
Scientific Consultants:	Dr. John Bevan
	Dr. Davie Duthie
	Dr. John Rostron
	Dr. Margaret Rostron
Diving Consultant:	Reg Vallintine
Picture Researcher:	Sophy Tahta
Keys Illustrator:	Edwina Hannam

Cover designed by Steven Woods

USBORNE
THE GREAT UNDERSEA SEARCH

Kate Needham

Illustrated by Ian Jackson

Designed by Andy Griffin

Scientific consultants: Dr. Margaret Rostron
and Dr. John Rostron

Diving consultant: Reg Vallintine

Series editor: Felicity Brooks

This snake lives in the mangrove swamps. Find out what else lives there on pages 24 and 25.

You can find penguins darting through the water off the Galapagos islands on pages 26 and 27.

Seabirds can dive deep to catch fish. Find these boobies on pages 26 and 27.

Learn about a diver's work under the sea on pages 22 and 23.

These undersea machines are used to repair oil rigs on pages 22 and 23.

Sea otters live in kelp forests. Find out who else lives there on pages 20 and 21.

Contents

3   About this book

4   Prehistoric seas

6   Shipwreck

8   Rocky shore

10   Icy seas

12   Pirate treasure

14   The big blue sea

16   The abyss

18   Coral dives

20   Kelp forest

22   Oil rigs

24   Seaside jungle

26   Volcanic islands

28   Answers

111   Index

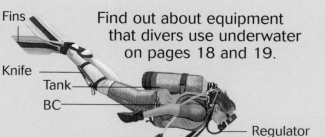

Many creatures that live in coral reefs have bright markings. You can find more of them on pages 18 and 19.

Fins

Knife

Tank

BC

Find out about equipment that divers use underwater on pages 18 and 19.

Regulator

Discover which weird creatures live at the bottom of the sea on pages 16 and 17.

About this book

Ammonites lived over 200 million years ago. Find some other ancient creatures on pages 4 and 5.

In this book you can find out about all sorts of exciting things that happen under the sea, and discover the animals and plants that live there. There are puzzles to solve too. This shows you how they work.

Find out where dangerous eels lurk on pages 6 and 7.

There are hundreds of things to find in each big picture. In real life the seas are much less crowded.

Around the outside of each big picture are lots of little ones.

The writing next to each picture tells you how many of that thing you can find in the big picture.

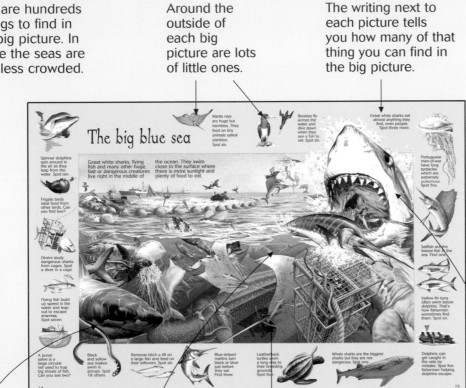

The big blue sea

Spinner dolphins spin around in the air as they leap from the water. Spot ten.

Frigate birds steal food from other birds. Can you find two?

Divers study dangerous sharks from cages. Spot a diver in a cage.

Flying fish build up speed in the water and leap out to escape enemies. Spot seven.

Great white sharks, flying fish and many other huge, fast or dangerous creatures live right in the middle of the ocean. They swim close to the surface where there is more sunlight and plenty of food to eat.

Manta rays are huge but harmless. They feed on tiny animals called plankton. Spot six.

Boobies fly across the water and dive down when they see a fish to eat. Spot six.

Great white sharks eat almost anything they find, even people. Spot three more.

Portuguese men-of-war have long tentacles which are extremely poisonous. Spot five.

Sailfish are the fastest fish in the sea. Find one.

Yellow fin tuna often swim below dolphins. That's how fishermen sometimes find them. Spot six.

A purse seine is a large circular net used to trap big shoals of fish. Can you see two?

Black and yellow sea snakes swim in groups. Spot 18 others.

Remoras hitch a lift on a large fish and feed on their leftovers. Spot six.

Blue-striped marlins turn black or blue just before they eat. Find three.

Leatherback turtles swim a long way to their breeding grounds. Spot four.

Whale sharks are the biggest sharks but they are not dangerous. Spot one.

Dolphins can get caught in the nets by mistake. Spot five fishermen helping dolphins escape.

14

15

You can only see part of this shark but it still counts.

This manta ray in the distance counts.

You will need to count all these snakes carefully.

This shark coming out of the picture is here instead of the little picture. You do not count it in your total.

The puzzle is to find all the things in the main picture. Some are easy, but others are tiny and partly hidden. Some animals look quite similar, so you will need to look very carefully to spot the difference. If you can't find something you can look up the answers on pages 28–31.

Discover what you might find in pools among the rocks on pages 8 and 9.

Spot the first submarine to cross under the Arctic ice on pages 10 and 11.

Find chests full of coins and more pirate treasure on pages 12 and 13.

Turn to pages 16 and 17 to find out about the submersibles that explore the ocean depths.

Sailfish are the fastest fish in the sea. You'll find them on pages 14 and 15.

Turn to pages 14 and 15 to find the most dangerous shark of all.

Ammonites used their tentacles to catch food. Find 13.

Prehistoric seas

Placodus had a very strong jaw. Find two.

Two hundred million years ago, dinosaurs ruled the land and giant creatures swam in the seas. Smaller ones lived there too. Some are still around today. Look closely to find 21 different creatures in this scene.

Banjo fish were ancient relatives of skates and rays. Can you see four more?

Ichthyosaurus gave birth under water. Find two adults and three babies.

Jellyfish lived up to 600 million years ago. Can you see four?

Giant sea turtles like archelon could hide inside their hard shells. Spot two.

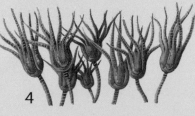

Sea lilies are animals not flowers. Can you find a group of them?

Rabbit fish get their name from their funny faces. Find two.

Elasmosaurus had a really long neck. Find one.

4

Tanystropheus lived at the edge of the sea and ate fish. Find two.

Pliosaurus was fast and fierce. It could attack large creatures. Spot one.

As a belemnite grew, its shell grew longer. Can you find four more?

Sponges looked much the same as they do now. Find three groups.

Some people think the Loch Ness monster is a plesiosaurus. Find three.

Starfish

Sea urchins

Sea cucumber

These creatures moved slowly across the sea floor. Spot three of each.

There were lots of different sharks. Find three like this one.

Lampshells were attached to the seabed by stalks. Find two groups of them.

King crabs are still around today. They turn upside-down to swim. Spot two more.

Geosaurus had sharp teeth and a long snout. Find two.

Shipwreck

All parts of a wreck are soon covered with coral. Can you find the anchor?

Reef sharks look dangerous but they rarely attack divers. Find three.

This ship was carrying bikes. Can you find three covered with coral?

Napoleon wrasses are large, friendly fish which often follow divers. Spot three.

Some wrecks have hidden treasure. There are 18 gold bars to find here.

When you dive down to explore a wreck, you never know what you may find. There may be strange creatures lurking in the depths, or treasure buried in the sand. This ship sank years ago. Now it's covered in coral.

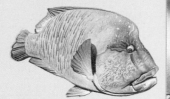

With an eye and a nostril on each side of its head, a hammerhead shark sees and smells well. Find four more.

Crocodile fish have shiny green eyes. Spot one hiding on the sea bed.

Corals of all shades grow on the wreck. Spot four pink clumps.

Parrot fish nibble the corals with their beak-like mouths. Spot three.

This diver is going down to explore the wreck. Can you find seven more?

Moray eels have very strong jaws. They hunt in the dark. Find four.

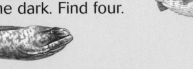

When they are scared, puffer fish blow up like spiky balloons. Can you see all four?

Spines

Lion fish have poisonous spines on their back. Spot two lion fish.

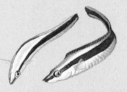

Cleaner fish clean the mouths and gills of larger fish. Spot four at work.

Blue spotted groupers like to live inside holes in the wreck. Find four.

These small fish recognize each other by their bright markings. Find 20 of each.

Angel fish

Anthias

Butterfly fish

Divers carry flashlights to see inside the darkest parts of a wreck. Spot four.

Glass fish swim around together in large groups called schools. Spot one school.

Rocky shore

Common starfish

Cushion star

"Bloody Henry"

There are many types of starfish. Most have five arms. Spot four of each of these.

Beadlet anemones close up tightly to keep moist until the sea returns. Spot 20.

Hermit crabs live in empty shells. They move house as they grow. Can you find two?

Limpets

Mussels

Some animals that live in shells cling to the rocks. Find five groups of each of these.

Kittiwakes live on the cliffs and fish in the sea. Can you count 50?

The sea comes in and out twice each day on this rocky shore. When it goes out, many creatures are left behind in pools among the rocks like this one. If you look closely you will find over 100 creatures here.

Grey seals have large eyes to see in cloudy water and thick fur to keep them warm. Spot nine.

Butterfish are long and thin with spots along their backs. Find four more.

With eyes on top of their heads, rock gobies can spot danger above. Find two.

Octopuses can squeeze into tiny spaces. Can you find one?

Some rocks have fossils like these ammonites in them. Find ten.

Oystercatchers use their sharp beaks to eat shellfish. Spot three more.

Shore crab

Edible crab

Velvet swimming crab

Crabs can give a painful nip if you pick them up. Find three of each type.

Blennies use their fins to walk to a new pool. Spot three.

Acorn barnacles attach themselves to any hard surface. Find some on rocks, crabs and mussels.

Prawns are hard to spot as they are almost transparent. Find seven.

Can you see a net and bucket that someone has left behind?

Squat lobsters have huge front legs that are bigger than their bodies. Spot two.

9

Bows

Icy seas

When polar bears swim, a layer of fat and thick fur keeps them warm in the icy water. Spot four.

Research ships have very strong bows to break through the ice. Spot one ship.

Beluga whales are called "sea canaries" because they sing to each other. Spot three.

Baby seals are called pups. They have fluffy white coats. Spot three.

Nautilus was the first submarine to cross the Arctic under the ice. Can you see it?

The Arctic Ocean is so cold that two-thirds of it is covered in ice all year round. Despite the freezing water, plenty of creatures live here. Scientists also visit to study the ice and learn about the world's changing climate.

Walruses can use their tusks to lever themselves out of the water. Find 15.

Scientists attach transmitters to some animals to find out how they live. Spot one.

Bearded seals use their long curly whiskers to find shellfish. Find three.

Male narwhals have a long spiral tusk that is actually a huge front tooth. Find eight.

Arctic terns fly from the very north to the very south of the world each year. Spot four.

Humpback whales sometimes leap right out of the water. Spot three.

Harp seal

Ringed seal

Ribbon seal

You can spot different seals by their markings. Find five of each of these.

Arctic skuas steal food from other birds. Spot two.

Puffins can use their wings like paddles to dive underwater for fish. Find three.

Killer whales catch seals by tipping up the ice so that they fall into the water. Spot three.

Little Auks gather in groups called rafts, while they look for food. Find ten.

Blue whales are probably the largest creatures that ever lived. Spot one.

Dolphin handle

Find a gold cup with dolphin handles.

Hand blower

Divers use hand blowers to blow away sand and uncover treasure. Spot two.

Barrel

Jar

Food for the ship's crew was stored in jars and barrels like these. Spot six of each.

Sometimes a diver makes a sketch of the ship. Spot a diver sketching.

Musket

Sword

Dagger

Pirate treasure

Pirates were looking for chests full of coins. Spot seven.

In the 16th century, Spanish ships called galleons sailed from the Americas to Spain laden with gold, silver and jewels. Many were attacked by pirates. These divers are exploring a ship that sank with all her treasure.

The ship's crew needed weapons to fight off the pirates. Find two of each of these.

Divers sometimes use metal detectors to help find buried treasures. Can you see one?

Find two gold plates.

Dividers

Sailors navigated by the sun and stars. Find these measuring instruments.

Camera

When divers find a wreck, they measure and photograph it. Can you see a camera?

Astrolabe

Sundial

Grid

Heavy things are attached to lifting bags which float to the surface. Find eight.

Silver ingot

Gold ingot

Gold and silver from South America were made into ingots in Mexico. Find seven silver and six gold ingots.

Small objects are brought to the surface in baskets. Can you spot six?

Find some divers measuring part of the wreck.

Cannon

Cannonballs

The captain used this whistle to give orders to his crew. Can you find it?

Gold locket

Rich people sailed as passengers. Find these six jewels.

Buckle covered with jewels

Rosary

Emerald cross

Emerald ring

Gold chain

Galleons built for battle had lots of cannons. Can you find 10 cannons and 20 cannonballs?

The big blue sea

Manta rays are huge but harmless. They feed on tiny animals called plankton. Spot six.

Spinner dolphins spin around in the air as they leap from the water. Spot ten.

Frigate birds steal food from other birds. Can you find two?

Divers study dangerous sharks from cages. Spot a diver in a cage.

Flying fish build up speed in the water and leap out to escape enemies. Spot seven.

A purse seine is a large circular net used to trap big shoals of fish. Can you see two?

Great white sharks, flying fish and many other huge, fast or dangerous creatures live right in the middle of the ocean. They swim close to the surface where there is more sunlight and plenty of food to eat.

Black and yellow sea snakes swim in groups. Spot 18 others.

Remoras hitch a lift on large fish and feed on their leftovers. Spot six.

Blue-striped marlins turn black or blue just before they eat. Find three.

Boobies fly across the water and dive down when they see a fish to eat. Spot six.

Great white sharks eat almost anything they find, even people. Can you spot three more?

Portuguese men-of-war have long tentacles which are extremely poisonous. Spot five.

Sailfish are the fastest fish in the sea. Find one.

Yellow fin tuna often swim below dolphins. That's how fishermen sometimes find them. Spot six.

Leatherback turtles swim a long way to their breeding grounds. Spot four.

Whale sharks are the biggest sharks but they are not dangerous. Spot one.

Dolphins can get caught in the nets by mistake. Spot five fishermen helping dolphins escape.

15

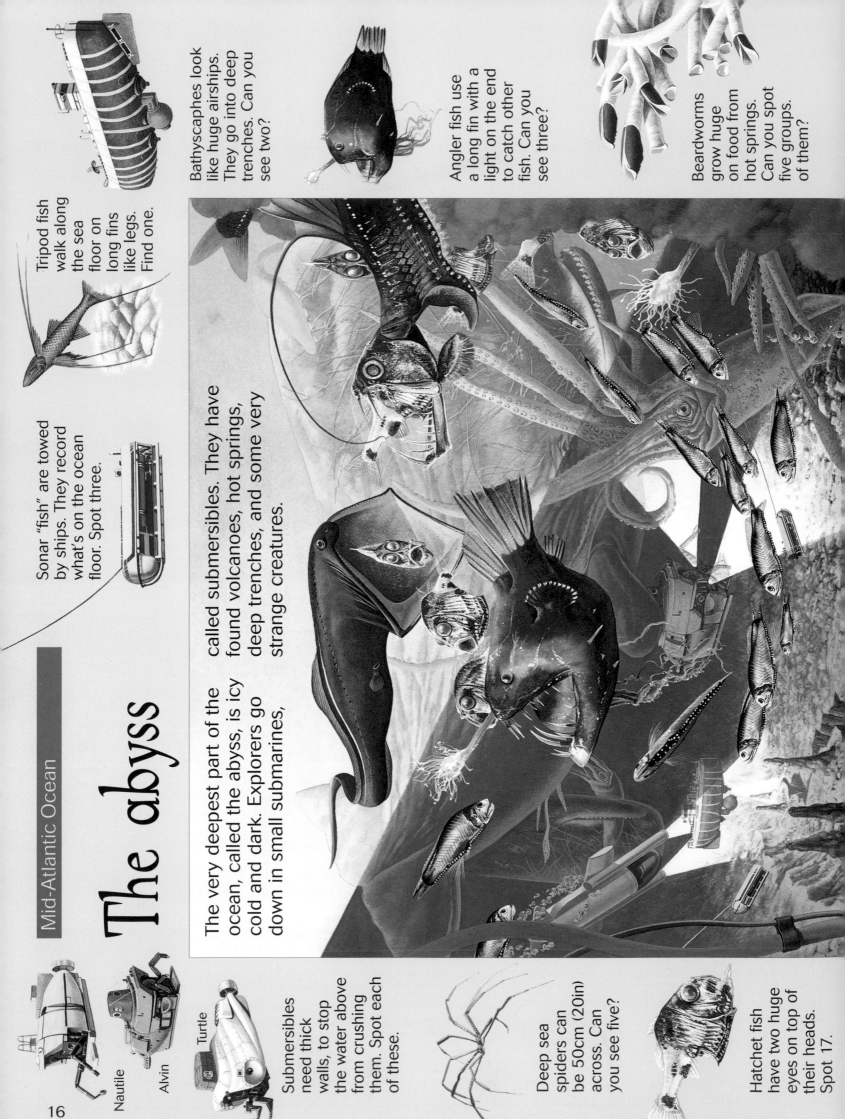

The abyss

The very deepest part of the ocean, called the abyss, is icy cold and dark. Explorers go down in small submarines, called submersibles. They have found volcanoes, hot springs, deep trenches, and some very strange creatures.

Bathyscaphes look like huge airships. They go into deep trenches. Can you see two?

Angler fish use a long fin with a light on the end to catch other fish. Can you see three?

Beardworms grow huge on food from hot springs. Can you spot five groups of them?

Tripod fish walk along the sea floor on long fins like legs. Find one.

Sonar "fish" are towed by ships. They record what's on the ocean floor. Spot three.

Nautile

Alvin

Turtle

Submersibles need thick walls, to stop the water above from crushing them. Spot each of these.

Deep sea spiders can be 50cm (20in) across. Can you see five?

Hatchet fish have two huge eyes on top of their heads. Spot 17.

16

Giant squid have huge eyes that are about 17 times the size of yours. Spot four.

Anemone

Crab

Vent fish

These strange creatures live and feed around the smokers. Find 20 of each.

Deep Flight is a submersible that can fly to the bottom fast. Can you see it?

Viper fish unhinge their jaws to gulp down large fish whole. Spot two.

Lantern fish have lights all along their bodies. Find 22.

Submersibles and ROVs have manipulator arms for picking things up. Spot five more.

Gulper eels swallow large fish with their wide mouths. Spot four.

Sperm whales dive deep for food, but they must swim to the surface to breathe. Can you find two?

ROVs are controlled by a cable from submersibles or ships. Can you see three?

Tall chimneys called black smokers grow up around hot springs. Can you find 15?

Coral dives

Millions of people dive for fun, and Australia's Great Barrier Reef is one of the best places to explore. The reef is made from the skeletons of billions of tiny creatures called corals. Can you find 15 divers here?

Fins help divers swim smoothly. Spot three yellow pairs.

Sea slugs are small but they have bright markings. Spot each of these.

Flash light

Underwater cameras need strong flash lights. Can you see four?

Sea wasp

Cone shell

Olive sea snake

These creatures are so poisonous, they can kill a person. Find one of each.

Giant clams grow very slowly and can live for 100 years. Can you find two?

Tank

Regulator

Divers breathe compressed air from tanks. Spot a diver with two tanks.

Snorkel

Can you find three blue snorkels?

Mask

Can you find a leaking mask, half full of water?

"Let's go up"

"I'm OK"

Divers use hand signals to "talk" to each other. Spot two divers making each of these signals.

Sea fan

Staghorn coral

Brain coral

Corals are animals though some look more like rocks. Spot four clumps of each type.

Divers wear weights on their belts to help them descend. Find a diver with six weights.

Clown fish hide in poisonous anemones. Find nine others.

Barracudas are curious and sometimes follow a diver. Spot five.

Divers add air to jackets called BCs to go up, and let it out to go down. Spot a pink BC.

Hundreds of small fish live in the reef. Find three of each of these.

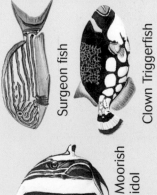

Surgeon fish

Clown Triggerfish

Moorish idol

Can you find four divers with knives?

Knife

Wetsuit

Can you see a diver in a short pink wetsuit like this one?

Depth gauge

Air

Consoles with dials show how much air is left and how deep it is. Find four.

Marker buoys on the surface show where the divers are. Can you see one?

Kelp forest

Giant kelp is the fastest growing plant in the world. It can grow 60cm (24in) in a day. Huge underwater kelp forests are home to thousands of creatures. People use the kelp, too, to make things such as ice cream or paint.

As kelp crabs get bigger, they shed their shell and grow a new one. Spot six.

Ocean goldfish guard their space in the kelp fiercely. Find 11.

Sea otters wrap up in kelp when they snooze on the surface. Find eight.

Sea stars stand on tiptoe to shed their eggs. Can you find two?

Bat rays glide through the forest on wing-like fins. Can you see three?

Gray whales shelter in the kelp to keep their babies safe. Spot a mother and her baby.

Sea snails eat their way up kelp plants. Spot 17.

Californian sealions are speedy swimmers and like to play. Spot three.

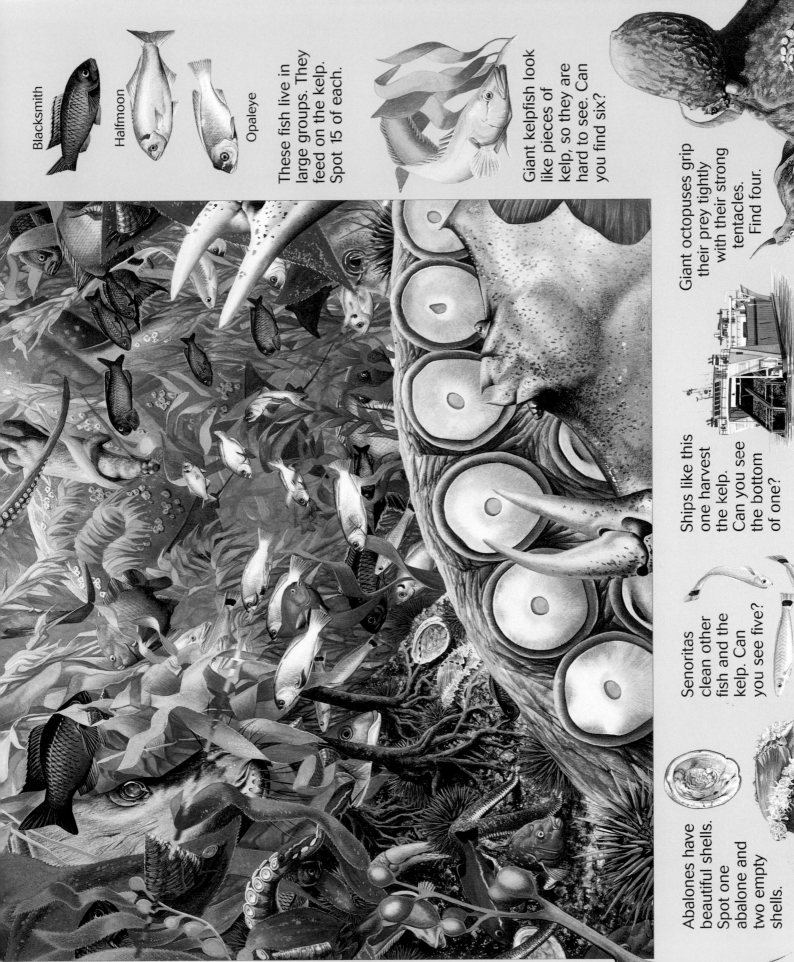

Blacksmith

Halfmoon

Opaleye

These fish live in large groups. They feed on the kelp. Spot 15 of each.

Giant kelpfish look like pieces of kelp, so they are hard to see. Can you find six?

Giant octopuses grip their prey tightly with their strong tentacles. Find four.

Ships like this one harvest the kelp. Can you see the bottom of one?

Senoritas clean other fish and the kelp. Can you see five?

Abalones have beautiful shells. Spot one abalone and two empty shells.

Young

Female

Male

Male, female and young sheephead wrasses all look different. Spot three of each.

Hungry sea urchins destroy the kelp. Find six red and six purple ones.

Each kelp plant has a holdfast which clings to the rock. Spot three more.

Oil rigs

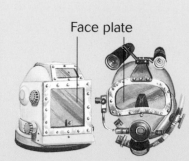

Face plate

Helmets let divers see and breathe easily. Find one with a square face plate.

Rigs are built on land and then towed out to sea. Can you find five of them?

When oil is found beneath the sea, giant rigs are built to bring it to the surface. Underwater machines, called ROVs, and deep sea divers check the rigs for damage and do repairs. It can be dangerous work.

Newtsuit

Hard suits stop the water pushing in on the diver. The Newtsuit has legs with special joints. Find two.

Wasp suit

Wasp suits have propellers to help them move around. Can you find five?

Conger eels have sharp teeth. They live in holes, so divers have to watch where they put their hands. Spot four.

Diving bells are used to lower divers into deep water. Can you find three?

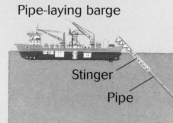

Pipe-laying barge

Stinger

Pipe

Pipes are laid by these special barges. Find one.

Special rods are heated up to cut metal. Spot three divers cutting.

22

Some seals are fierce and try to chase divers away. Spot five.

Diving support vessel

Moon pool

Diving bell

Diving equipment is lowered into the water from a diving support vessel. Find one.

Diver in hardsuit

Airbags are used to support heavy things in the water. Spot ten.

Tools are lowered from the surface in these baskets. Find five.

Work ROV

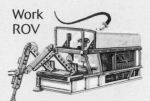

Different types of ROVs (remotely operated vehicles) are used for each job. Work ROVs have mechanical arms. Spot three.

Eyeball ROVs have cameras which film any damage and repairs. Spot six.

Gas   Hot water

Phone line

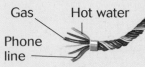

Umbilicals join divers to a bell, bringing them hot water and gas. Spot six.

Mussels grow all over the rig and sometimes have to be cleaned off. Spot five groups of them.

Find 12 of each of these fish.

Pollack

Cod

Water jet pumps are used for tasks such as cleaning. Can you see one?

23

Seaside jungle

Ospreys catch fish with their large feet and claws. Spot one.

A glossy ibis uses its long beak to catch shellfish, insects and even snakes. Spot four.

Otters paddle on the surface and dive down for food. Find three.

Soldier crabs can recognize each other by their blue shells. Spot 22.

The tangled roots of mangrove trees make a perfect home for many creatures. These trees grow in hot parts of the world where a river meets the sea. Their roots reach down into the water to help prop them up.

Saltwater crocodiles are very dangerous and very large. Find three more.

Dog-headed sea snakes slither through the water hunting for fish and crabs. Spot seven.

Mudskippers can use their fins like arms to drag themselves along the mud. Spot 25.

Oyster

Chama

The mangrove roots are a good place for shellfish to breed. Spot 21 of each of these.

Young tripletail fish hide on their sides near the surface. They look like dead leaves. Spot 12.

Ocean creatures often visit the mangroves to feed on plants. Can you spot two turtles?

Crab-eating macaques use their strong teeth to open shellfish. Spot two more.

When kingfishers spot a fish, they plunge head first after it. Find five.

Proboscis monkeys like to swim. They often dive into the water to cool off. Spot five.

Some mangrove seedlings float for a year before planting themselves in the mud. Find 14.

Unlike most frogs, crab-eating frogs are happy in salt water. Can you spot three?

Male fiddler crabs use their enormous claw to fight off rivals. Find three.

Volcanic islands

Spot four swallow-tailed gulls.

A few of these volcanic islands are still erupting. Can you see one?

The Galápagos islands were formed by volcanoes erupting at the bottom of the sea. They are a long way from any other land. Some creatures that live here are found nowhere else in the world.

Sealions surf in the waves for fun, but must watch out for sharks. Find five.

Flightless cormorants hold their little wings out to dry after a dive. Spot one.

Common dolphin

Spotted dolphin

Dolphins come to the surface frequently for air. Find two of each of these types.

Pelicans scoop up fish in the pouch under their beaks. Spot two.

Squid have two long arms and eight short ones. Find three.

A male frigate bird blows up his throat pouch to attract a mate. Spot two.

Pilot whales nudge their babies to the surface to breathe. Spot a mother and baby.

Albatrosses live mostly at sea. They only come to land to breed. Find one.

Fur seals get too hot in the midday sun, so they lie in the water to cool off. Spot two.

Red-footed booby

Blue-footed booby

Boobies make spectacular dives from 25m (82ft) high. Find four of each.

Sally lightfoot crabs have red shells and blue bellies. Spot 25.

These penguins use their stubby wings to "fly" through the water. Spot eight.

Tiger sharks hunt alone. They swim all day, only stopping to eat. Can you find one?

Marine iguanas are lizards that can swim. They have to lie in the sun to warm up. Find 14 more.

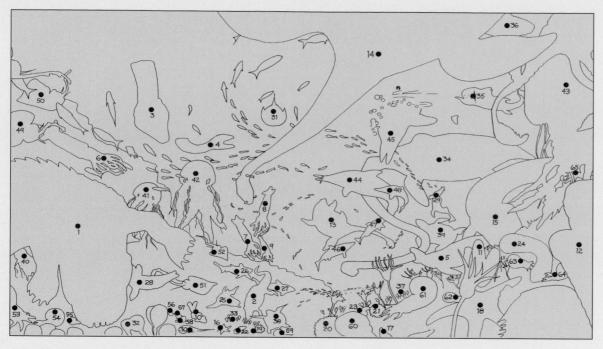

Prehistoric seas 4–5

Placodus 1 2
Tanystropheus 3 4
Pliosaurus 5
Belemnites 6 7 8 9
Sponges 10 11 12
Plesiosaurus 13
    14 15
Starfish 16 17 18
Sea urchins 19
    20 21
Sea cucumbers 22
    23 24
Sharks 25 26 27
Geosaurus 28 29
King crabs 30 31
Lampshells 32 33
Elasmosaurus 34
Rabbit fish 35 36
Sea lilies 37
Archelon 38 39
Jellyfish 40 41
    42 43
Ichthyosaurus:
    adults 44 45
    babies 46 47 48

Banjo fish 49 50
    51 52
Ammonites 53
    54 55 56 57 58
    59 60 61 62 63
    64 65

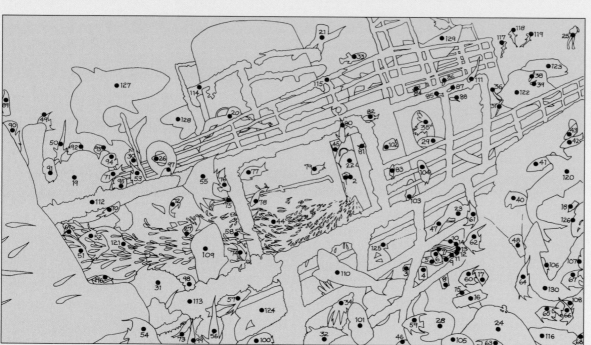

Shipwreck 6–7

Gold bars 1 2 3 4 5
    6 7 8 9 10 11 12
    13 14 15 16 17 18
Divers 19 20 21 22
    23 24 25
Moray eels 26 27
    28 29
Puffer fish 30 31
    32 33
Lion fish 34 35
Cleaner fish 36 37
    38 39
Blue spotted
groupers 40 41
    42 43
Glass fish 44
Flashlights 45 46
    47 48
Angel fish 49 50 51
    52 53 54 55 56
    57 58 59 60 61
    62 63 64 65 66
    67 68
Anthias 69 70 71
    72 73 74 75 76
    77 78 79 80 81
    82 83 84 85 86
    87 88

Butterfly fish 89 90
    91 92 93 94 95
    96 97 98 99 100
    101 102 103 104
    105 106 107 108
Parrot fish 109
    110 111
Pink corals 112 113
    114 115
Crocodile fish 116
Hammerhead sharks
    117 118 119 120
Napoleon wrasses
    121 122 123
Bikes 124 125 126
Reef sharks 127 128
    129
Anchor 130

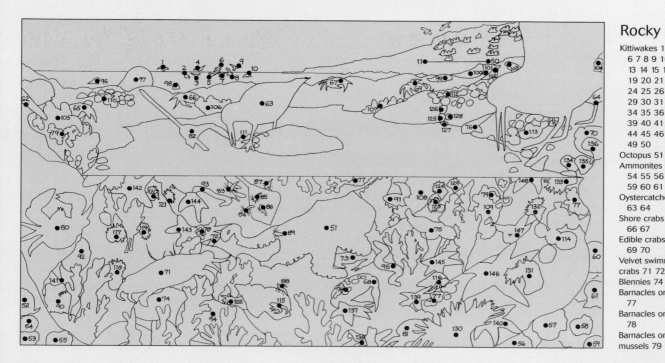

Rocky shore 8–9

Kittiwakes 1 2 3 4 5
    6 7 8 9 10 11 12
    13 14 15 16 17 18
    19 20 21 22 23
    24 25 26 27 28
    29 30 31 32 33
    34 35 36 37 38
    39 40 41 42 43
    44 45 46 47 48
    49 50
Octopus 51
Ammonites 52 53
    54 55 56 57 58
    59 60 61
Oystercatchers 62
    63 64
Shore crabs 65
    66 67
Edible crabs 68
    69 70
Velvet swimming
crabs 71 72 73
Blennies 74 75 76
Barnacles on rocks
    77
Barnacles on crabs
    78
Barnacles on
mussels 79

Squat lobsters 80 81
Net and bucket 82
Prawns 83 84 85 86
    87 88 89
Rock gobies 90 91
Butterfish 92 93
    94 95
Grey seals 96 97 98
    99 100 101 102
    103 104
Mussels 105 106
    107 108 109
Limpets 110 111 112
    113 114
Hermit crabs 115 116
Beadlet anemones
    117 118 119 120
    121 122 123 124
    125 126 127 128
    129 130 131 132
    133 134 135 136
"Bloody Henry"
starfish 137 138
    139 140
Cushion star 141 142
    143 144
Common starfish
    145 146 147 148

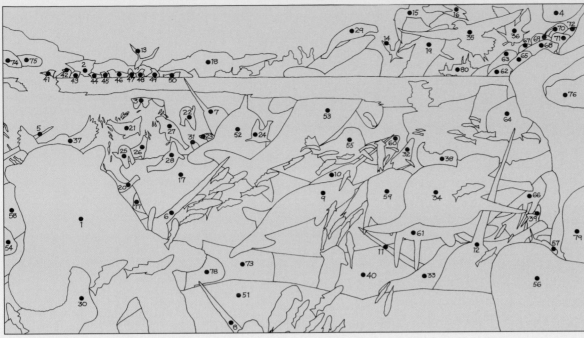

Icy seas 10–11

Polar bears 1 2 3 4
Narwhals 5 6 7 8 9
  10 11 12
Arctic terns 13 14
  15 16
Humpback whales
  17 18 19
Harp seals 20 21
  22 23 24
Ringed seals 25 26
  27 28 29
Ribbon seals 30 31
  32 33 34
Arctic skuas 35 36
Puffins 37 38 39
Blue whale 40
Little auks 41 42 43
  44 45 46 47 48
  49 50
Killer whales 51
  52 53
Bearded seals 54
  55 56
Transmitter 57
Walruses 58 59 60
  61 62 63 64 65
  66 67 68 69 70
  71 72

Nautilus 73
Baby seals 74 75 76
Beluga whales 77
  78 79
Research ship 80

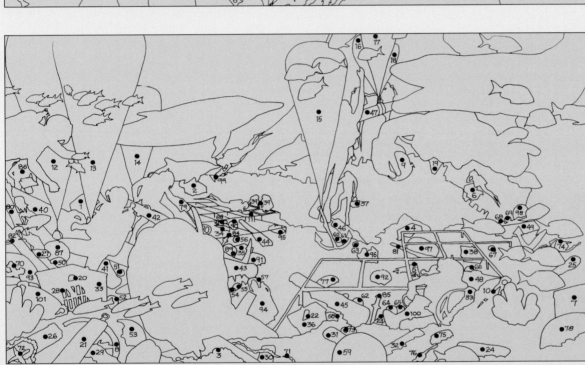

Pirate treasure 12–13

Chest of coins 1 2 3
  4 5 6 7
Astrolabe 8
Sundial 9
Dividers 10
Camera 11
Lifting bags 12 13 14
  15 16 17 18 19
Gold ingots 20 21
  22 23 24 25
Silver ingots 26 27
  28 29 30 31 32
Baskets 33 34 35
  36 37 38
Divers measuring 39
Cannons 40 41 42
  43 44 45 46 47
  48 49
Cannonballs 50 51
  52 53 54 55 56
  57 58 59 60 61
  62 63 64 65 66
  67 68 69
Emerald cross 70
Gold chain 71
Rosary 72
Emerald ring 73
Gold locket 74

Buckle 75
Whistle 76
Gold plates 77 78
Metal detector 79
Muskets 80 81
Swords 82 83
Daggers 84 85
Diver sketching 86
Jars 87 88 89 90
  91 92
Barrels 93 94 95 96
  97 98
Hand blowers 99
  100
Gold cup 101

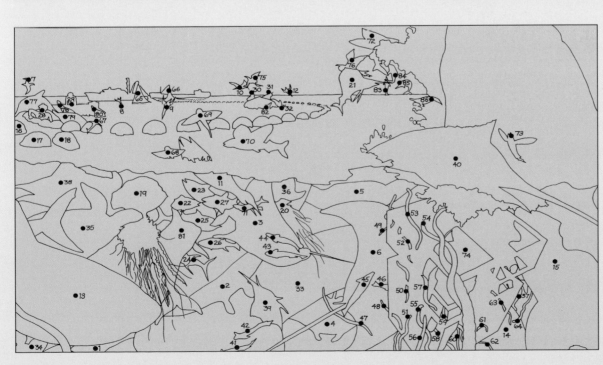

The big blue sea 14–15

Manta rays 1 2 3 4
  5 6
Boobies 7 8 9 10
  11 12
Great white sharks
  13 14 15
Portuguese men-
  of-war 16 17 18
  19 20
Sailfish 21
Yellow fin tuna 22
  23 24 25 26 27
Fishermen 28 29 30
  31 32
Whale shark 33
Leatherback turtles
  34 35 36 37
Marlins 38 39 40
Remoras 41 42 43
  44 45 46
Sea snakes 47
  48 49 50 51 52
  53 54 55 56 57
  58 59 60 61 62
  63 64
Purse seine nets
  65 66

Flying fish 67 68 69
  70 71 72 73
Diver in cage 74
Frigate birds 75 76
Spinner dolphins 77
  78 79 80 81 82
  83 84 85 86

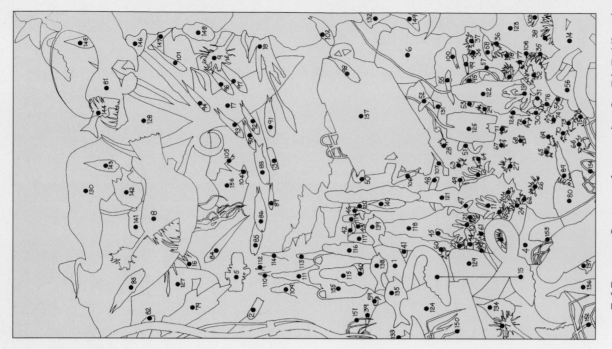

The abyss 16–17

Sonar "fish" 1 2 3
Tripod fish 4
Bathyscaphes 5 6
Angler fish 7 8 9
Beardworms 10 11
  12 13 14
Giant squid 15 16
  17 18
Anemones 19 20 21
  22 23 24 25 26
  27 28 29 30 31
  32 33 34 35 36
  37 38
Vent fish 39 40 41
  42 43 44 45 46
  47 48 49 50 51
  52 53 54 55 56
  57 58
Crabs 59 60 61
  62 63 64 65 66
  67 68 69 70 71
  72 73 74 75 76
  77 78
Deep Flight 79
Viper fish 80 81
Lantern fish 82
  83 84 85 86 87
  88 89 90 91 92
  93 94 95 96 97

98 99 100 101
  102 103
Manipulator arms
  104 105 106
  107 108
Black smokers 109
  110 111 112 113
  114 115 116 117
  118 119 120 121
  122 123
ROVs 124 125 126
Sperm whales 127
  128
Gulper eels 129 130
  131 132
Hatchet fish 133 134
  135 136 137 138
  139 140 141 142
  143 144 145 146
  147 148 149
Deep sea spiders
  150 151 152
  153 154
Submersibles:
  Turtle 155
  Alvin 156
  Nautile 157

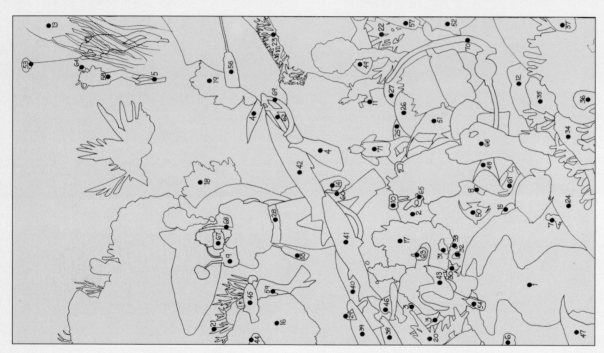

Coral dives 18–19

Giant clams 1 2
Yellow fins 3 4 5
Sea slugs 6 7 8
Cameras 9 10 11 12
Sea wasp 13
Olive sea snake 14
Cone shell 15
Coral:
  Sea fan 16 17
  18 19
  Staghorn 20 21
  22 23
  Brain 24 25 26 27
Diver with six
weights 28
Clown fish 29 30
  31 32 33 34 35
  36 37
Barracudas 38 39
  40 41 42
Pink BC 43
Clown triggerfish 44
  45 46
Surgeon fish 47
  48 49
Moorish idol 50
  51 52
Marker buoy 53

Consoles 54 55
  56 57
Diver in short pink
wetsuit 58
Knives 59 60 61 62
Divers' signals:
  "Let's go up"
  63 64
  "I'm OK" 65 66
Leaking mask 67
Blue snorkels 68
  69 70
Diver with two tanks
  71

Kelp forest 20–21

Sea otters 1 2 3 4 5
  6 7 8
Ocean goldfish 9 10
  11 12 13 14 15 16
  17 18 19
Kelp crabs 20 21 22
  23 24 25
Sea stars 26 27
Bat rays 28 29 30
Blacksmiths 31 32
  33 34 35 36 37
  38 39 40 41 42
  43 44 45
Halfmoons 46 47 48
  49 50 51 52 53
  54 55 56 57 58
  59 60
Opaleyes 61 62 63
  64 65 66 67 68
  69 70 71 72 73
  74 75
Giant kelpfish 76 77
  78 79 80 81
Giant octopuses 82
  83 84 85
Ship 86
Senoritas 87 88 89
  90 91

Abalone 92
Empty abalone shells
  93 94
Holdfasts 95 96 97
Red sea urchins 98
  99 100 101 102
  103
Purple sea urchins
  104 105 106 107
  108 109
Sheephead wrasses:
  male 110 111 112
  female 113 114 115
  young 116 117 118
Sealions 119
  120 121
Sea snails 122 123
  124 125 126 127
  128 129 130 131
  132 133 134 135
  136 137 138
Gray whales:
  mother 139
  baby 140

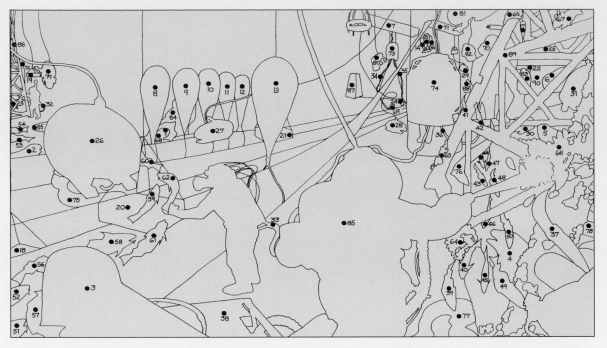

Oil rigs 22–23

Helmet with square
face plate 1
Seals 2 3 4 5 6
Diving support
vessel 7
Airbags 8 9 10 11
  12 13 14 15 16 17
Tool baskets 18 19
  20 21 22
Work ROVs 23
  24 25
Eyeball ROVs 26 27
  28 29 30 31
Umbilicals 32 33 34
  35 36 37
Water jet pump 38
Pollack 39 40 41 42
  43 44 45 46 47
  48 49 50
Cod 51 52 53 54
  55 56 57 58 59
  60 61 62
Mussels 63 64 65
  66 67
Divers cutting 68
  69 70
Pipe-laying barge 71

Diving bells 72
  73 74
Conger eels 75 76
  77 78
Wasp suits 79 80 81
  82 83
Newtsuits 84 85
Rigs 86 87 88
  89 90

Seaside jungle 24–25

Osprey 1
Tripletail fish 2 3 4
  5 6 7 8 9 10 11
  12 13
Turtles 14 15
Crab-eating
macaques 16 17
Kingfishers 18 19 20
  21 22
Proboscis monkeys
  23 24 25 26 27
Male fiddler crabs
  28 29 30
Crab-eating frogs 31
  32 33
Mangrove seedlings
  34 35 36 37 38
  39 40 41 42 43
  44 45 46 47
Oysters 48 49 50
  51 52 53 54 55
  56 57 58 59 60
  61 62 63 64 65
  66 67 68

Chama 69 70 71 72
  73 74 75 76 77
  78 79 80 81 82
  83 84 85 86 87
  88 89
Mudskippers 90 91
  92 93 94 95 96
  97 98 99 100 101
  102 103 104 105
  106 107 108 109
  110 111 112 113 114
Dog-headed sea
snakes 115 116 117
  118 119 120 121
Saltwater crocodiles
  122 123 124
Soldier crabs
  125 126 127 128
  129 130 131 132
  133 134 135 136
  137 138 139 140
  141 142 143 144
  145 146
Otters 147 148 149
Glossy ibis 150 151
  152 153

Volcanic islands 26–27

Swallow-tailed gulls
  1 2 3 4
Pilot whale:
  adult 5
  baby 6
Albatross 7
Fur seals 8 9
Red-footed boobies
  10 11 12 13
Blue-footed boobies
  14 15 16 17
Sally lightfoot crabs
  18 19 20 21 22
  23 24 25 26 27
  28 29 30 31 32
  33 34 35 36 37
  38 39 40 41 42
Marine iguanas 43
  44 45 46 47 48
  49 50 51 52 53
  54 55 56
Tiger shark 57
Penguins 58 59 60
  61 62 63 64 65
Male frigate birds
  66 67
Squid 68 69 70
Pelicans 71 72

Spotted dolphins
  73 74
Common dolphins
  75 76
Cormorant 77
Sealions 78 79 80
  81 82
Volcanic island
erupting 83

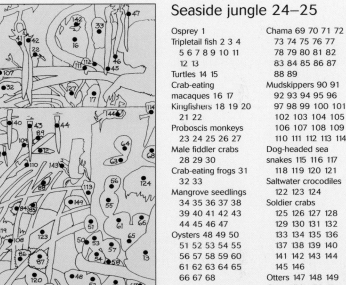

USBORNE
THE BIG
BUG
SEARCH

Caroline Young

Illustrated by Ian Jackson

Designed by Andy Dixon

Edited by Kamini Khanduri

Contents

34	About this book	52	Deep in the jungle
36	Homes and gardens	54	Minibeast safari
38	Cactus city	56	Insect city
40	Island paradise	57	Busy beehive
42	Dazzling display	58	Around the world
44	Between the trees	59	Big bug puzzle
46	Water world	60	Answers
48	In the woods	62	Answers
50	Swamp life	111	Index

About this book

This is a puzzle book all about bugs. If you look hard, you'll find beetles, butterflies, spiders, snails, slugs and hundreds of other creepy-crawlies from all around the world. This is how the puzzles work.

Some bugs live in and around our homes. Find out which ones on pages 36 and 37.

See inside these trapdoor spiders' burrows in the scorching desert on pages 38 and 39.

This cockroach from Madagascar makes a strange noise. Find out what it is on pages 40 and 41.

There are about 100 bugs in each big picture. In real life, there wouldn't be as many in one place at the same time.

Around the outside of each big picture, there are lots of little pictures.

The writing next to each little picture tells you how many of that bug to look for in the big picture.

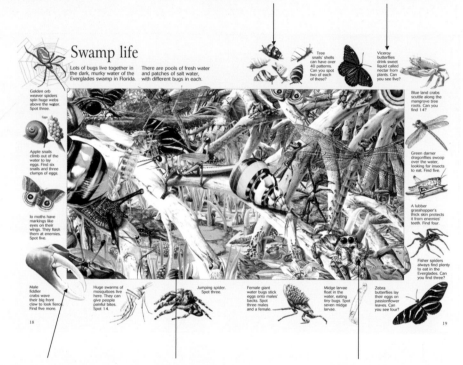

This crab coming out of the big picture counts as a little picture too.

This part of a snail's shell counts as one snail.

A spider is about to eat this mosquito, but the mosquito still counts.

Some of the bugs are very easy to spot, but some are tiny, or hidden against their background. If you get really stuck, you'll find all the answers on pages 60–63.

On pages 42 and 43, you can find out why you should steer clear of these wandering spiders from Peru.

These pretty emperor gum moths live among the eucalyptus trees in Australia. See what else does on pages 44 and 45.

Worker bees have busy lives. Find out about the jobs they do in a beehive on page 57.

Queen termites are much bigger than any other termites. On page 56, you can see a queen inside her home.

In South Africa, a gang of assassin bugs can be very dangerous. You'll discover why on pages 54 and 55.

Hidden extras

You'll find one of these animals hiding somewhere on each page. On pages split into two halves (pages 40–41, 52–53 and 56–57), there's one animal in each half.

Aardvark

Orang-utan

Mouse

Blue tree boa

Green tree frog

Kudu

Ring-tailed lemur

Hedgehog

Bandicoot

Great white heron

Cat

Tapir

Alligator

Burrowing owl

Hairy bird-eating spiders live deep in the jungle. Find out more about them on pages 52 and 53.

Young bugs

Young bugs are often called nymphs or larvae. They may look very different from their parents. Here's how a dragonfly grows up.

Adult flying

Dragonflies lay eggs in or near water. Each egg hatches into a dragonfly nymph.

Nymph

As it grows, the nymph loses its skin. The last time it does this, it becomes an adult.

Adult emerging

Lubber grasshoppers live in the Everglades swamp in the USA. You'll find them on pages 50 and 51.

Pond snails make life easier for all the animals living in a pond. Find out how on pages 46 and 47.

Woods are home to hundreds of different minibeasts. You can see some of them on pages 48 and 49.

Homes and gardens

Not all minibeasts live in wild places. Many live in gardens, parks, and even in and around houses. This is a picture of a house in Britain. Can you spot 158 creatures here?

Snails leave sticky trails which show where they have been. Can you track down ten?

Most fleas drink the blood of animals. Some also drink human blood. Spot ten.

Female garden spiders are bigger than males and often eat them after mating. Spot eight spiders.

Houseflies' mouths are like a mop, soaking up liquid food. Find ten houseflies.

Cinnabar moth

Caterpillar

Unlike most moths, cinnabar moths fly by day. Spot seven moths and six caterpillars.

Lacewings sleep somewhere warm all winter. They turn brown while they sleep. Find 14.

Cockroaches have flat bodies. They can squeeze under things to hide. Spot 11.

Male

Female common blue butterfly

Only male common blue butterflies are really blue. Spot four of each sex.

Honeybees carry yellow pollen from flowers in "baskets" on their back legs. Can you find ten?

Zebra spiders creep up behind their victims and pounce on them. Find five.

Their name means "100 feet" but no centipedes have that many. Can you spot six?

Wasps like anything sweet, including our food. They'll sting you if you annoy them. Spot 13.

Devil's coach-horses arch their bodies to scare off enemies. Spot six coach-horses.

Earwigs lift their fierce-looking tails if they are scared, but they can't hurt you. Spot nine.

Tail

Greenflies suck the juice out of plants for their food. Can you spot 17?

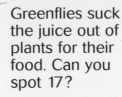

Spittle bugs blow air and spit out of their bottoms to make foam. Find eight bugs hidden in foam.

37

Cactus city

This dry desert in the north of Mexico doesn't look like a very comfortable home, but thousands of bugs live here. Many stay in cool underground burrows during the hot day.

Some people keep Mexican red-kneed bird-eating spiders as pets. Can you find four here?

Painted grasshoppers are named after their bright-looking bodies. Can you spot ten?

Harvester ants collect seeds and store them deep underground. Find 15 busy ants.

Hercules beetles are some of the biggest insects in the world. Can you spot six?

Whip scorpions have a long, thin tail like a whip. It can't hurt you, though. Spot five.

Ant-lion larvae dig pits in the sand. When other bugs fall in, they eat them. Find three.

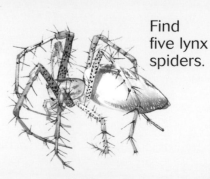

Find five lynx spiders.

Tarantula hawk wasps lay their eggs on tarantula spiders' bodies. Can you find seven of them?

When insects pass a trapdoor spider's home, it flips up its "door" and grabs them. Spot four.

Scorpions lurk in cool burrows until the sun sets. Then they go hunting. Spot six.

Giant red velvet mites hatch out after rain and rush around looking for food. Spot ten.

Some honey ants hang upside down in the nest. Their tummies are full of honey. Spot 13.

Blister beetles sting your skin if you touch them. Find four blister beetles.

Yucca moths only lay their eggs in a yucca plant's flowers. Spot five yucca moths.

Tarantula. Find six.

A southern black widow spider will only bite you if you annoy it. Can you spot four?

Island paradise

The island of Madagascar is home to many bugs that aren't found anywhere else. The bugs on this page live in thick, dry woods. Those on the opposite page live in a rainforest.

Brilliant red dragonflies flit through the trees in the rainforest. Spot four.

Striped flatworms slither across the forest floor after it has rained. Can you find four?

Weevils often have long noses, but giraffe-necked weevils have long necks. Find four.

Huge emperor dragonflies catch insects flying past. Can you spot six of them?

Some stick insects grow fake "moss" on their bodies as a disguise. Find three.

Thorn spiders look like prickly jewels in their huge webs. Find four.

Giant millipedes can be poisonous, so few animals eat them. Can you find five?

This praying mantis nymph is very well disguised. Can you spot four?

Green lynx spiders blend in with their leafy surroundings. Find four.

Pill millipedes can't run from enemies. They roll into a ball instead. Spot six.

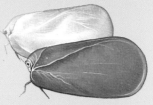

Rosea bugs look a little like leaves. If a bird pecks one, the whole group flies off. Find 27.

Hairy weevils only live in Madagascar. Spot seven of each of these.

Longhorn beetles lay their eggs in dead wood. Later, their larvae eat it. Find seven.

Hissing cockroaches hiss by blowing air out of two holes in their tummies. Find five.

Can you find four shield bug adults and four nymphs?

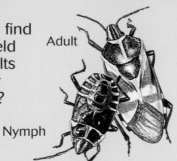

Adult

Nymph

Spot six butterflies with their wings open and five with their wings shut.

41

Dazzling display

Some of the most beautiful insects in the world live in rainforests, but they are often hard to spot. Can you find 95 minibeasts in this rainforest in Peru, in South America?

Find nine leaf beetles.

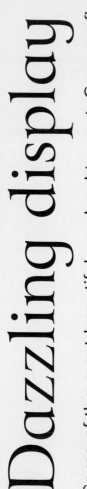

A wandering spider's bite is so poisonous it can kill a person. Can you find two?

Thornbugs look like thorns. Their disguise fools hungry birds. Spot ten.

When Hamadryas butterflies fly, their wings make clicking noises. Can you spot four?

Some assassin bugs have spiky bodies. Enemies find them hard to chew. Can you find seven?

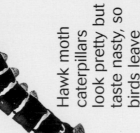

Hawk moth caterpillars look pretty but taste nasty, so birds leave them alone. Spot five.

Many gorgeous grasshoppers live in these forests. Find three of each of these kinds.

Long-legged stilt bugs have long, skinny legs that look a little like stilts. Find five.

These bright bugs must taste good because local people eat them. Find six.

Male harlequin beetles guard females with their long front legs. Find seven harlequin beetles.

Female

Male

This grasshopper hides by staying still and hoping it looks like a stick. Spot three.

Bark bugs are hard to spot. They blend into the background. Find seven.

Morpho butterfly. Spot four.

Male Hercules beetles use their horns to push other males away. Spot four.

Leafcutter ants eat fungus. They help it grow by covering it with chewed leaves. Find 16.

43

Between the trees

All kinds of amazing bugs live in the thick eucalyptus forests of eastern Australia. Ants as big as your toes go marching past, and poisonous spiders lurk in dark corners.

Emperor gum moths only lay their eggs on eucalyptus trees. Find three.

Sawfly larvae wave their heads and spit bitter liquid at their enemies. Find nine.

Female redback spiders are much more poisonous than males. Can you spot three?

Processionary moth caterpillars leave a long silk thread behind them. Find 11.

Fierce Sydney funnel-web spiders only live near the city of Sydney. Spot four.

Bulldog ants are the biggest, fiercest ants in the world. Can you spot 12 of them?

Giant stick insects unfold their wings to give enemies a shock. Can you find four?

Net throwing spiders throw a net of silk over their victims. Spot two more.

Some crickets flash their bright backs at enemies to scare them. Find five.

Bogong moths can eat whole fields of grain if they get together. Spot four.

Common grass yellow butterflies sip water from puddles in hot weather. Spot 23.

Emperor gum moth caterpillars have bright spikes to warn enemies off. Find four.

Gliding spiders can stretch out two flaps of skin and glide through the air. Find four.

Some people dig moth caterpillars called "witchetty grubs" out of tree trunks and eat them. Find six.

There are over 450 different types of shield bugs in Australia. Can you spot nine of this kind?

Monarch butterflies can fly up to 130km (80 miles) in one day. Find five.

Water world

Ponds are perfect homes for many small creatures. They are often nurseries for young insects too. Can you spot 121 minibeasts in this North American pond?

Fisher spiders crawl down plants, catch fish, then haul them up to eat. Spot eight.

Tube

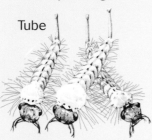

Mosquito larvae dangle under the surface of ponds. They breathe through a tube. Spot seven.

Backswimmers swim upside down, using their back legs as oars. Find six.

Stoneflies can't fly well, so they sit beside the water most of the time. Spot nine.

Damselflies can't walk well. They use their legs to grab hold of plants. Spot seven.

Water striders skim lightly across the surface of the pond. Spot eight water striders.

Fishermen put fake caddisflies on their hooks to attract fish. Spot six real caddisflies.

Pond snails do a very useful job. They eat plants and make the water much clearer. Find 11.

Great diving beetle larvae bite their victims and then suck out their insides. Find five.

Water scorpions lurk just below the surface, grabbing passing insects. Spot six.

Dragonfly nymphs have jaws that shoot out to crunch up food. Can you spot five?

Caddisfly larvae are safe inside a case covered with pebbles and shells. Find five.

Whirligig beetles can look into the air and under the water at the same time. Find 15.

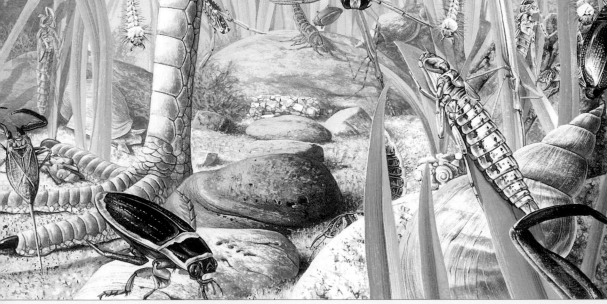

Great diving beetles have strong back legs to help them swim and dive. Spot ten.

Water stick insects breathe air through a narrow breathing tube. Find five stick insects.

Adult mayflies never eat. They just mate, lay eggs and die. Find nine.

47

In the woods

If you walked through this wood in northern France, thousands of eyes might be watching you. Tiny creatures make their homes up in the trees, or down on the ground.

Male stag beetles fight with their sharp antlers, but rarely hurt each other. Find six.

Wood ants squirt acid out of their bottoms to attack enemies. Can you spot 20?

Crane flies have six legs. They can survive losing one or two of them. Find eight.

Hedge snails are easy for birds to spot, so they try to stay hidden. Find six snails.

Darter dragonflies flit through the trees in woodland clearings. Can you spot three?

Male empid flies give females a bug wrapped in silk while they mate. Find 12.

Bumblebees fly from flower to flower, collecting pollen. Spot four bumblebees.

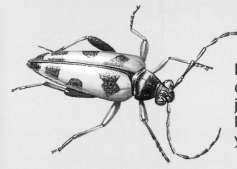

Antenna

Longhorn beetles don't have horns, just antennae that look like them. Can you spot seven?

Burying beetles lay their eggs next to a dead animal. When the eggs hatch into larvae, they eat it. Spot ten.

Hornets chew bark to make a soggy mixture. They use it to build nests. Find four.

The amount of purple you can see on a purple emperor butterfly's wings depends on the light. Spot six.

Bark beetles lay their eggs in tree bark. When the eggs hatch, the larvae eat the bark. Find 11.

Large black slugs slither along the woodland floor, leaving a slimy trail. Spot seven.

Poplar hawk moths can see in the dark, so they fly at night. Find five.

Male horseflies drink plant juices but females need to drink animals' blood. Spot four.

Crab spiders lie in wait for insects in flowers. Then they attack and kill them. Spot three.

49

Swamp life

Lots of bugs live together in the dark, murky water of the Everglades swamp in Florida.

There are pools of fresh water and patches of salt water, with different bugs in each.

Golden orb weaver spiders spin huge webs above the water. Spot three.

Eggs

Apple snails climb out of the water to lay eggs. Find six snails and three clumps of eggs.

Io moths have markings like eyes on their wings. They flash them at enemies. Spot five.

Male fiddler crabs wave their big front claw to look fierce. Find five more.

Huge swarms of mosquitoes live here. They can give people painful bites. Spot 14.

Jumping spider. Spot three.

Tree snails' shells can have over 40 patterns. Can you spot two of each of these?

Viceroy butterflies drink sweet liquid called nectar from plants. Can you see five?

Blue land crabs scuttle along the mangrove tree roots. Can you find 14?

Green darner dragonflies swoop over the water, looking for insects to eat. Find five.

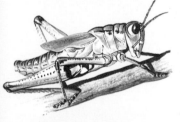

A lubber grasshopper's thick skin protects it from enemies' teeth. Find four.

Fisher spiders always find plenty to eat in the Everglades. Can you find three?

Female giant water bugs stick eggs onto males' backs. Spot three males and a female.

Midge larvae float in the water, eating tiny bugs. Spot seven midge larvae.

Zebra butterflies lay their eggs on passionflower leaves. Can you see four?

Deep in the jungle

The jungles of southeast Asia are as busy by night as they are by day. The left-hand page shows who comes out in the daytime and the right-hand page shows the night.

Hairy bird-eating spiders really do eat birds. They can climb trees too. Find four.

Fireflies' tummies light up, then flash on and off. Find 11.

Cockchafer beetle. Find seven.

Stay away from red centipedes. Their bites are very painful. Can you spot five?

Atlas moths are the largest moths in the world. Look hard and try to find three.

Snails slither around the jungle. Find three of each of these two kinds of snails.

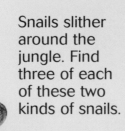

Longicorn beetles use their long feelers to explore the jungle. Can you see five?

Loepa moths have no tongues. They don't live long enough to need food. Find four.

Lantern bugs got their name because they often flutter around people's lanterns. Spot ten.

Flat-backed millipedes eat fungi that grows on trees. Can you find five of them?

These shield bugs taste horrible, so other animals don't eat them. Find seven.

Brilliant jewel beetles like lying on leaves in the warm sunshine. Find eight.

Termites march to and fro on the jungle floor. Can you spot 16 termites here?

Male cicadas make a chirping sound with a part of their tummies. Find five.

Birdwing butterflies are as big as a hand when their wings are open. Spot four.

Weaver ants make nests by sticking leaves together with spit. Can you spot 12?

Nephila spiders spin webs out of pale yellow silk. Can you spot four of them?

Minibeast safari

People go on expeditions, or safaris, to see the wildlife of Africa. They may not see the thousands of bugs that live there too. Spot 118 in this picture of part of South Africa.

Male rhinoceros beetles have a horn like a rhinoceros. Can you see five?

Tsetse flies drink other creatures' blood through a tube-shaped mouth. Find ten.

Swallowtail butterfly

Swallowtail caterpillar

These caterpillars wave smelly horns at enemies. Can you spot five caterpillars and three butterflies?

Potter wasps put caterpillars in their nests as food for their larvae. Find five potter wasps.

African land snails are the largest snails in the world. Can you spot four of them?

African assassin bugs work as a team, killing other insects. Find five.

Longhorn beetles chew their way into tree trunks. Find seven longhorn beetles.

African moon moths flash the eye-like markings on their wings at enemies. Spot three.

Hanging flies hang upside down from twigs with their long, skinny legs. Find eight.

Monarch butterflies eat plants that make their flesh taste horrible. Find four.

Histerid beetles like eating dung, or the bodies of dead animals. Find 21.

Ground beetles can squirt burning acid out of their bottoms. Can you spot four?

Processionary moth. Find three.

Processionary moth caterpillars wriggle along the ground in a long line. Spot ten.

Stalk-eyed flies got their name from their eyes. It's easy to see why. Find four.

A swarm of hungry locusts can eat a whole crop in hours. Spot 11 locusts.

If you disturb a praying mantis, it might wave its back wings at you. Spot six.

Insect city

Termites live in huge family groups. They build a mound of mud, spit and dung, and make a nest inside. This is what the nest looks like.

Termite mound

Only the queen termite lays eggs. She can lay over 30,000 a day. Can you find her?

All the king termite does is mate with the queen. Can you spot him?

Worker

Eggs

Worker termites take eggs to parts of the nest called nurseries. Find four nurseries.

Worker

Larvae

The eggs hatch into pale larvae. Worker termites care for them. Find 23 larvae.

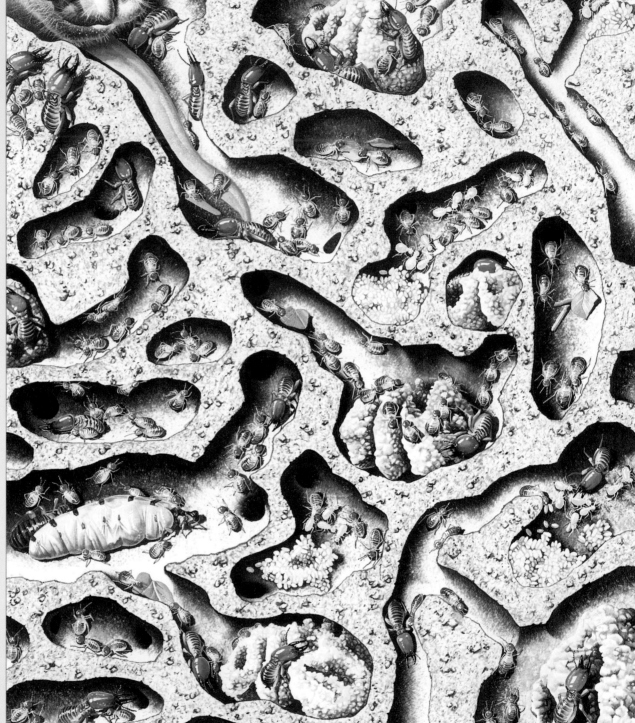

Soldier termites keep guard. They bite enemies, or squirt liquid at them. Spot 20.

Workers carry leaves into the nest in their mouths. Spot seven doing this job.

Fungus grows in "fungus gardens" in the nest. The termites eat it. Find six gardens.

Busy beehive

People keep honeybees in hives. The bees collect nectar and pollen from flowers. They eat the pollen and make the nectar into honey.

Beehive

Only the long, slim queen bee can lay eggs. Can you find her?

Drones are big male bees. They mate with the queen, then get pushed out of the hive. Find seven.

Huddling around the queen to keep her safe.

Carrying balls of pollen on their back legs.

Feeding larvae that are growing in the hive.

Worker bees do several jobs. Find three workers doing each of the things above.

Bees build little wax boxes called cells in the hive. Spot the cells being used for these things.

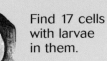

Find 17 cells with larvae in them.

Find ten cells full of pollen.

Worker bees sometimes spit food into another bee's mouth. Find one doing this.

Find 14 cells full of honey.

Find 12 cells with bee eggs in them.

57

Around the world

This map of the world shows the places where all the bugs in this book live.

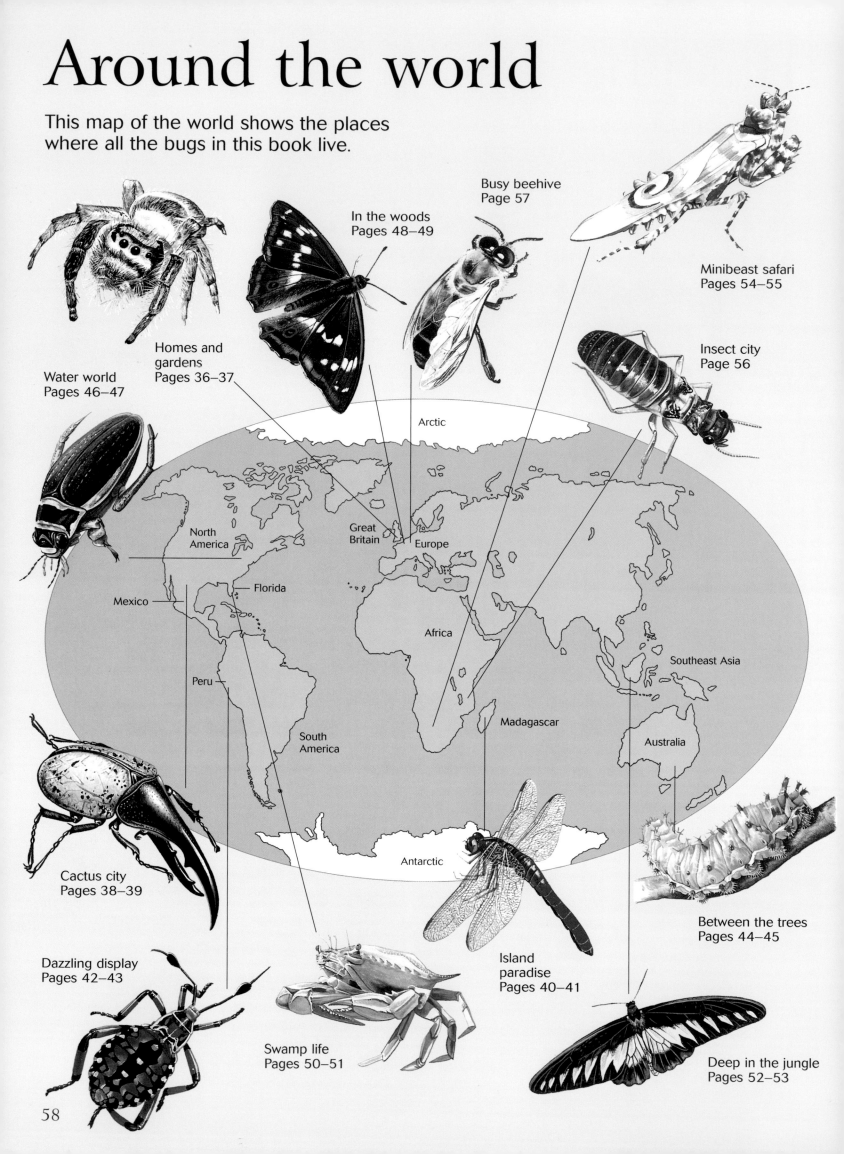

In the woods
Pages 48–49

Busy beehive
Page 57

Minibeast safari
Pages 54–55

Insect city
Page 56

Homes and gardens
Pages 36–37

Water world
Pages 46–47

Arctic

North America

Great Britain

Europe

Mexico

Florida

Africa

Southeast Asia

Peru

Madagascar

Australia

South America

Antarctic

Cactus city
Pages 38–39

Between the trees
Pages 44–45

Dazzling display
Pages 42–43

Island paradise
Pages 40–41

Swamp life
Pages 50–51

Deep in the jungle
Pages 52–53

Big bug puzzle

You've seen all these bugs earlier in the book, but can you remember anything about them? To do this puzzle, you may need to look back and find which page they're on. If you get stuck, the answers are on page 63.

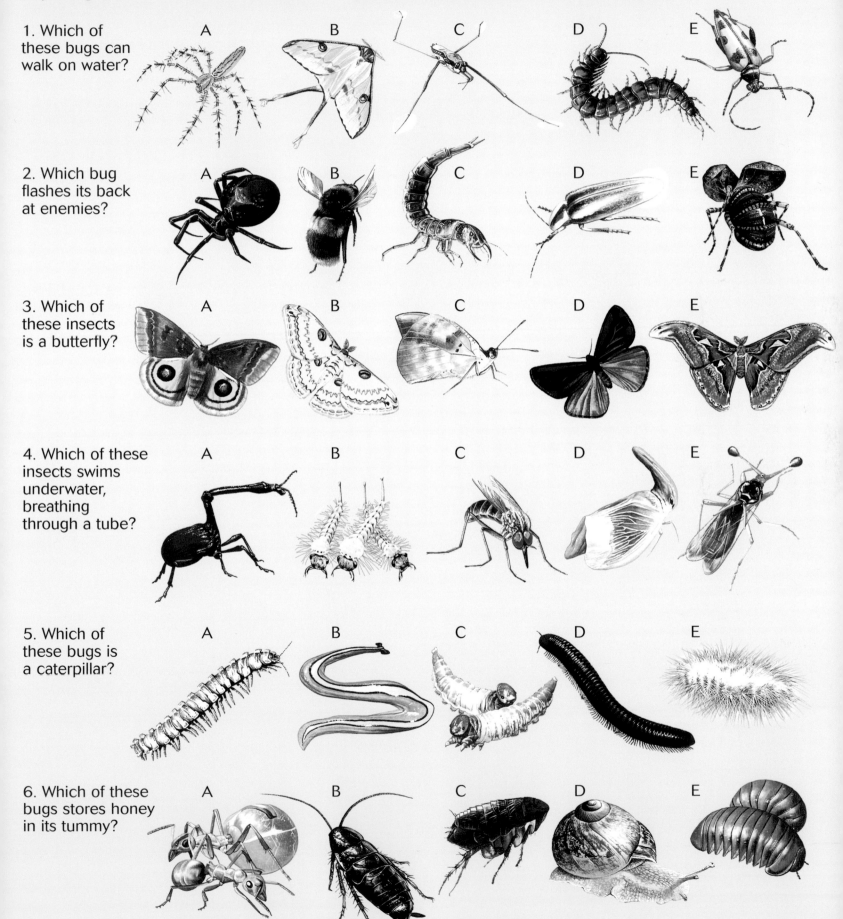

1. Which of these bugs can walk on water?

A   B   C   D   E

2. Which bug flashes its back at enemies?

A   B   C   D   E

3. Which of these insects is a butterfly?

A   B   C   D   E

4. Which of these insects swims underwater, breathing through a tube?

A   B   C   D   E

5. Which of these bugs is a caterpillar?

A   B   C   D   E

6. Which of these bugs stores honey in its tummy?

A   B   C   D   E

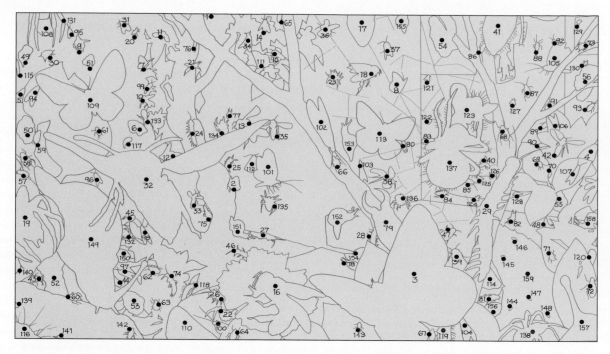

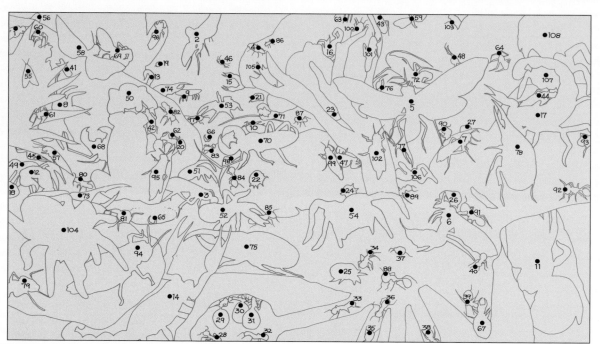

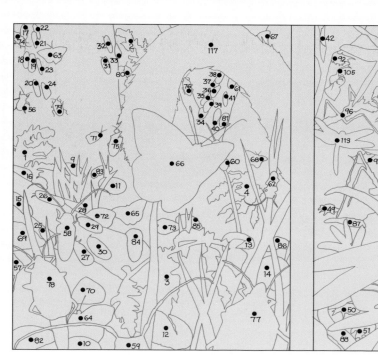

Homes and gardens 36–37

Male common blue butterflies 1 2 3 4
Female common blue butterflies 5 6 7 8
Honeybees 9 10 11 12 13 14 15 16 17 18
Zebra spiders 19 20 21 22 23
Centipedes 24 25 26 27 28 29
Wasps 30 31 32 33 34 35 36 37 38 39 40 41 42
Devil's coach-horses 43 44 45 46 47 48
Spittle bugs 49 50 51 52 53 54 55 56
Greenflies 57 58 59 60 61 62 63 64 65 66 67 68 69 70 71 72 73
Earwigs 74 75 76 77 78 79 80 81 82
Cockroaches 83 84 85 86 87 88 89

90 91 92 93
Lacewings 94 95 96 97 98 99 100 101 102 103 104 105 106 107
Cinnabar moths 108 109 110 111 112 113 114
Cinnabar moth caterpillars 115 116 117 118 119 120
Houseflies 121 122 123 124 125 126 127 128 129 130
Garden spiders 131 132 133 134 135 136 137 138
Fleas 139 140 141 142 143 144 145 146 147 148
Snails 149 150 151 152 153 154 155 156 157 158
Cat 159

Cactus city 38–39

Tarantula hawk wasps 1 2 3 4 5 6 7
Trapdoor spiders 8 9 10 11
Scorpions 12 13 14 15 16 17
Giant red velvet mites 18 19 20 21 22 23 24 25 26 27
Honey ants 28 29 30 31 32 33 34 35 36 37 38 39 40
Blister beetles 41 42 43 44
Black widow spiders 45 46 47 48
Tarantulas 49 50 51 52 53 54
Yucca moths 55 56 57 58 59
Lynx spiders 60 61 62 63 64
Ant-lion larvae 65 66 67
Whip scorpions 68 69 70 71 72

Hercules beetles 73 74 75 76 77 78
Harvester ants 79 80 81 82 83 84 85 86 87 88 89 90 91 92 93
Painted grasshoppers 94 95 96 97 98 99 100 101 102 103
Red-kneed bird-eating spiders 104 105 106 107
Burrowing owl 108

Island paradise 40–41

Praying mantis nymphs 1 2 3 4
Lynx spiders 5 6 7 8
Pill millipedes 9 10 11 12 13 14
Rosea bugs 15 16 17 18 19 20 21 22 23 24 25 26 27 28 29 30 31 32 33 34 35 36 37 38 39 40 41
Yellow hairy weevils 42 43 44 45 46 47 48
Brown hairy weevils 49 50 51 52 53 54 55
Longhorn beetles 56 57 58 59 60 61 62
Butterflies with open wings 63 64 65 66 67 68
Butterflies with shut wings 69 70 71 72 73
Shield bug adults 74 75 76 77

Shield bug nymphs 78 79 80 81
Hissing cockroaches 82 83 84 85 86
Giant millipedes 87 88 89 90 91
Thorn spiders 92 93 94 95
Stick insects 96 97 98
Emperor dragonflies 99 100 101 102 103 104
Giraffe-necked weevils 105 106 107 108
Flatworms 109 110 111 112
Red dragonflies 113 114 115 116
Ring-tailed lemur 117
Blue tree boa 118

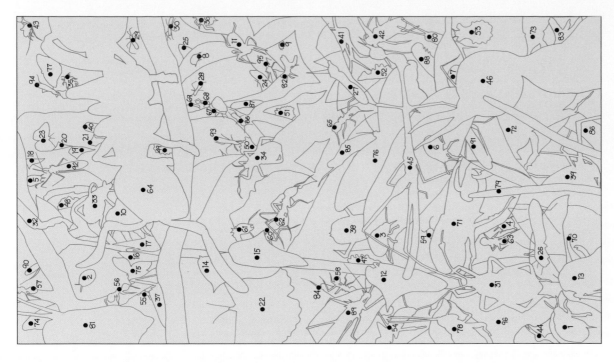

Dazzling display 42–43

Leaf beetles 1 2 3 4 5 6 7 8 9

Wandering spiders 10 11

Thornbugs 12 13 14 15 16 17 18 19 20 21

Hamadryas butterflies 22 23 24 25

Stilt bugs 26 27 28 29 30

Bright bugs 31 32 33 34 35 36

Harlequin beetles 37 38 39 40 41 42 43

Grasshoppers 44 45 46

Bark bugs 47 48 49 50 51 52 53

Leafcutter ants 54 55 56 57 58 59 60 61 62 63 64 65 66 67 68 69

Hercules beetles 70 71 72 73

Morpho butterflies 74 75 76 77

Black and yellow grasshoppers 78 79 80

Yellow, black and red grasshoppers 81 82 83

Hawk moth caterpillars 84 85 86 87 88

Assassin bugs 89 90 91 92 93 94 95

Tapir 96

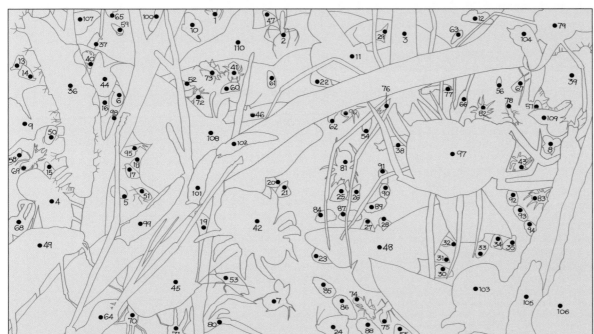

Between the trees 44–45

Net throwing spiders 1 2 3

Crickets 4 5 6 7 8

Bogong moths 9 10 11 12

Common grass yellow butterflies 13 14 15 16 17 18 19 20 21 22 23 24 25 26 27 28 29 30 31 32 33 34 35

Emperor gum moth caterpillars 36 37 38 39

Gliding spiders 40 41 42 43

Monarch butterflies 44 45 46 47 48

Shield bugs 49 50 51 52 53 54 55 56 57

Witchetty grubs 58 59 60 61 62 63

Giant stick insects 64 65 66 67

Bulldog ants 68 69 70 71 72 73 74 75 76 77 78 79

Sydney funnel-web spiders 80 81 82 83

Processionary moth caterpillars 84 85 86 87 88 89 90 91 92 93 94

Redback spiders 95 96 97

Sawfly larvae 98 99 100 101 102 103 104 105 106

Emperor gum moths 107 108 109

Bandicoot 110

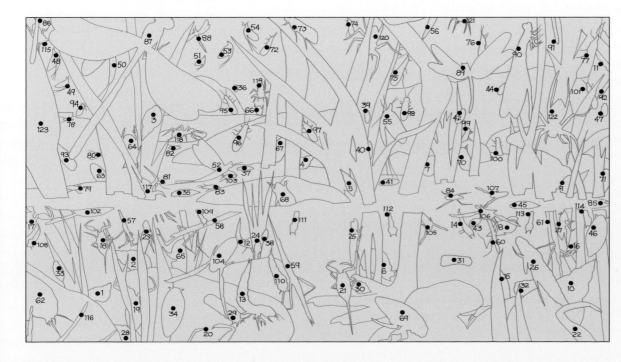

Water world 46–47

Pond snails 1 2 3 4 5 6 7 8 9 10 11

Great diving beetle larvae 12 13 14 15 16

Water scorpions 17 18 19 20 21 22

Dragonfly nymphs 23 24 25 26 27

Caddisfly larvae 28 29 30 31 32

Whirligig beetles 33 34 35 36 37 38 39 40 41 42 43 44 45 46 47

Mayflies 48 49 50 51 52 53 54 55 56

Water stick insects 57 58 59 60 61

Great diving beetles 62 63 64 65 66 67 68 69 70 71

Caddisflies 72 73 74 75 76 77

Water striders 78 79 80 81 82 83 84 85

Damselflies 86 87 88 89 90 91 92

Stoneflies 93 94 95 96 97 98 99 100 101

Backswimmers 102 103 104 105 106 107

Mosquito larvae 108 109 110 111 112 113 114

Fisher spiders 115 116 117 118 119 120 121 122

Great white heron 123

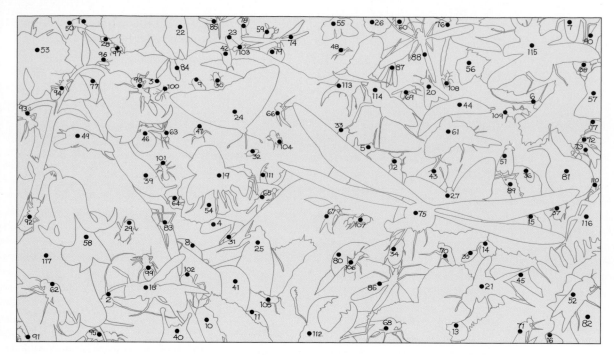

In the woods 48–49

Longhorn beetles 1
2 3 4 5 6 7
Burying beetles 8 9
10 11 12 13 14 15
16 17
Hornets 18 19 20
21
Purple emperor
butterflies 22 23 24
25 26 27
Bark beetles 28 29
30 31 32 33 34
35 36 37 38
Slugs 39 40 41 42
43 44 45
Crab spiders 46 47
48
Horseflies 49 50 51
52
Poplar hawk moths
53 54 55 56 57
Bumblebees 58 59
60 61
Empid flies 62 63
64 65 66 67 68
69 70 71 72 73
Darter dragonflies
74 75 76

Hedge snails 77 78
79 80 81 82
Crane flies 83 84 85
86 87 88 89 90
Wood ants 91 92 93
94 95 96 97 98
99 100 101 102
103 104 105 106
107 108 109 110
Stag beetles 111 112
113 114 115 116
Hedgehog 117

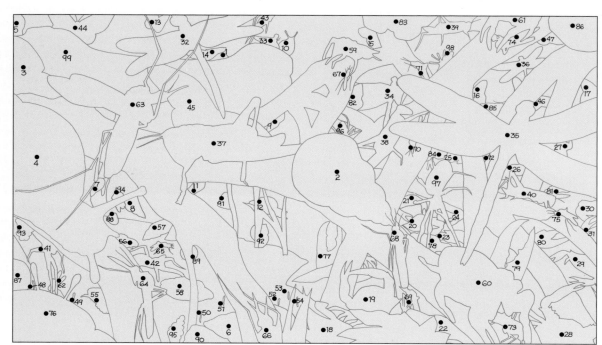

Swamp life 50–51

Tree snails 1 2 3 4
5 6 7 8 9 10 11
12
Viceroy butterflies 13
14 15 16 17
Blue land crabs 18
19 20 21 22 23
24 25 26 27 28
29 30 31
Green darner
dragonflies 32 33
34 35 36
Lubber grasshoppers
37 38 39 40
Fisher spiders 41 42
43
Zebra butterflies 44
45 46 47
Midge larvae 48 49
50 51 52 53 54
Giant water bugs 55
56 57 58
Jumping spiders 59
60 61
Mosquitoes 62 63
64 65 66 67 68
69 70 71 72 73
74 75

Fiddler crabs 76 77
78 79 80 81
Io moths 82 83 84
85 86
Apple snails 87 88
89 90 91 92
Apple snail eggs 93
94 95
Golden orb weaver
spiders 96 97 98
Alligator 99

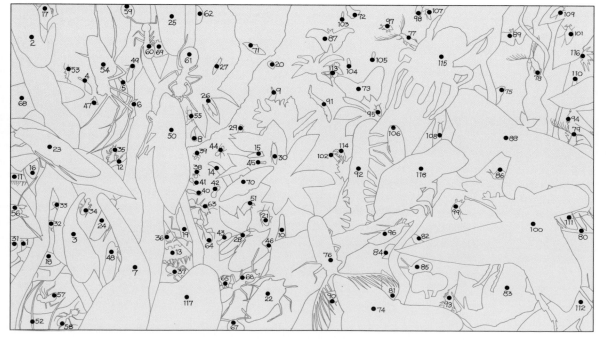

Deep in the jungle 52–53

Lantern bugs 1 2 3
4 5 6 7 8 9 10
Flat-backed
millipedes 11 12 13
14 15
Shield bugs 16 17
18 19 20 21 22
Jewel beetles 23 24
25 26 27 28 29
30
Termites 31 32 33
34 35 36 37 38
39 40 41 42 43
44 45 46
Cicadas 47 48 49
50 51
Nephila spiders 52
53 54 55
Weaver ants 56 57
58 59 60 61 62
63 64 65 66 67
Birdwing butterflies
68 69 70 71
Loepa moths 72 73
74 75
Longicorn beetles
76 77 78 79 80
Yellow snails 81 82
83

Brown snails 84 85
86
Atlas moths 87 88
89
Red centipedes 90
91 92 93 94
Cockchafer beetles
95 96 97 98 99
100 101
Fireflies 102 103
104 105 106 107
108 109 110 111
112
Hairy bird-eating
spiders 113 114 115
116
Orang-utan 117
Green tree frog 118

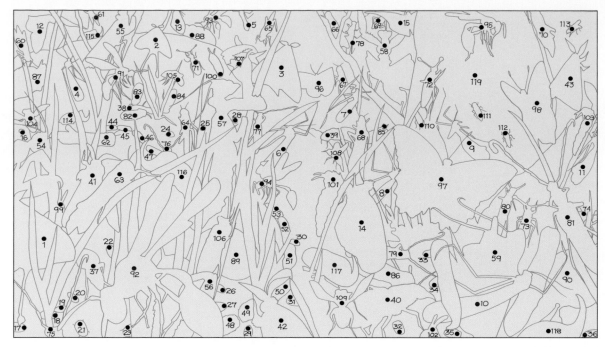

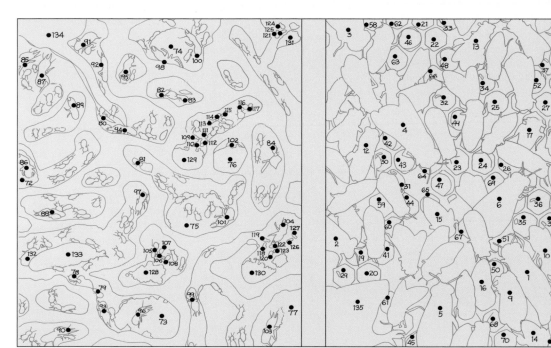

Minibeast safari 54–55

African moon moths
1 2 3

Hanging flies 4 5 6
7 8 9 10 11

Monarch butterflies
12 13 14 15

Histerid beetles 16
17 18 19 20 21
22 23 24 25 26
27 28 29 30 31
32 33 34 35 36

Ground beetles 37
38 39 40

Processionary moths
41 42 43

Processionary moth
caterpillars 44 45
46 47 48 49 50
51 52 53

Praying mantids 54
55 56 57 58 59

Locusts 60 61 62
63 64 65 66 67
68 69 70

Stalk-eyed flies 71
72 73 74

Longhorn beetles 75
76 77 78 79 80
81

African assassin
bugs 82 83 84 85
86

African land snails
87 88 89 90

Potter wasps 91 92
93 94 95

Swallowtail
butterflies 96 97 98

Swallowtail butterfly
caterpillars 99 100
101 102 103

Tsetse flies 104 105
106 107 108 109
110 111 112 113

Rhinoceros beetles
114 115 116 117
118

Kudu 119

Insect city 56

Fungus gardens 72
73 74 75 76 77

Workers carrying
leaves 78 79 80 81
82 83 84

Soldier termites 85
86 87 88 89 90
91 92 93 94 95
96 97 98 99 100
101 102 103 104

Larvae 105 106
107 108 109 110
111 112 113 114 115
116 117 118 119
120 121 122 123
124 125 126 127

Nurseries 128 129
130 131

King termite 132

Queen termite 133

Aardvark 134

Busy beehive 57

Queen bee 1

Drones 2 3 4 5 6 7
8

Workers huddling
around the queen 9
10 11

Workers carrying
balls of pollen 12 13
14

Workers feeding
larvae 15 16 17

Worker spitting 18

Pollen cells 19 20
21 22 23 24 25

26 27 28

Egg cells 29 30 31
32 33 34 35 36
37 38 39 40

Larvae cells 41 42
43 44 45 46 47
48 49 50 51 52
53 54 55 56 57

Honey cells 58 59
60 61 62 63 64
65 66 67 68 69
70 71

Mouse 135

Big bug puzzle on page 59:
1C 2E 3C 4B 5E 6A

63

Usborne
THE GREAT
ANIMAL
SEARCH

Caroline Young

Illustrated by Ian Jackson
Designed by Andy Dixon

Scientific consultants: Dr. Margaret Rostron
and Dr. John Rostron
Series editor: Felicity Brooks

Blue whales are the biggest animals of all. You'll find one on pages 98 and 99.

Gardens are busy places. Pages 100 and 101 show you what might live there.

Pigs are just one of the animals you can see on pages 102 and 103.

Find out how a shingle-backed skink gets rid of enemies on pages 96 and 97.

Bright flame shrimps live on the Barrier Reef, on pages 94 and 95.

Tigers hunt in the thick jungles of India. Find out what else lives there on pages 92 and 93.

Contents

67   About this book
68   Back in time
70   Conifer forests
72   Steamy swamps
74   Dusty deserts
76   The Arctic
78   Under the sea
80   Rainforests
82   Hot and dry
84   African plains
86   Hidden homes
88   By the sea
90   Mountains
92   Light and dark
94   Magical world
96   Out and about
98   Antarctica
100 A closer look
102 On the farm
104 Answers
110 Around the world
111 Index

Snow leopards hunt in the highest places. Turn to pages 90 and 91 to find out where.

Starfish live on the seashore. Find out what else does on pages 88 and 89.

Squirrels are just one of the animals living in woods like the one on pages 86 and 87.

The huge African plains on pages 84 and 85 are home to fast-running cheetahs.

About this book

This creature is a Stegosaurus. Turn to pages 68 and 69 to find out about more kinds of dinosaurs.

You can find out about more than 300 different kinds of animals in this book, but it's not just a book about animals. It's a puzzle book, too. This is how the puzzles work, plus a few tips to help you solve them.

There are around 100 animals in each big picture. In real life, there would not be as many in the same place at the same time.

Around the outside of each big picture, there are lots of little pictures.

The writing next to each one tells you how many of that animal you can find in the big picture.

Skunks make their home in the thick conifer forests on pages 70 and 71.

American bald eagles glide above the swamps on pages 72 and 73.

Mexican red-kneed spiders live in the Sonoran Desert on pages 74 and 75.

African plains

East Africa

This giraffe's horn counts as one giraffe.

A lioness has killed this zebra, but the zebra still counts.

This baby baboon counts as one baboon.

These elephants in the distance count.

The puzzly part is finding all the animals. Some are easy to spot, but some are tiny, or hidden against their background. On some pages there's another puzzle too. If you get stuck, you'll find all the answers on pages 104–109. Every single animal shown in the little pictures that you can find in each big picture counts in your total.

Polar bears live in the Arctic. Find out what else lives there on pages 76 and 77.

Camels live in the scorching Sahara Desert. Spot more of them on pages 82 and 83.

Sloths find it easy to hide in the thick Amazon Rainforest on pages 80 and 81.

Octopuses are just one of the sea creatures you can find out about on pages 78 and 79.

Back in time

Tyrannosaurus ate other dinosaurs. It was a ferocious hunter. Find three.

Alamosaurus lived on marshy land, munching plants. Find two.

Seventy million years ago, part of North America probably looked like this. Animals called dinosaurs lived here. There are 51 creatures for you to find in this picture. Can you spot them all?

Pteranodon flew on big wings of stretched-out skin. Find two others here.

Parasaurolophus had a curved, bony tube on its head. Can you spot three?

Struthiomimus looked a bit like an ostrich without feathers. Spot seven.

Pachycephalosaurus had a bony lump on its head for head-butting enemies. Can you find three?

Maiasauras laid their eggs in nests. Find one Maiasaura.

Deinosuchus' name means "terrible crocodile". Spot two.

Styracosaurus had a bony collar around its neck. Find one.

Ankylosaurus swung its bony tail like a club. Find two.

Quetzalcoatlus was a pterosaur, or "flying lizard". It was as big as a small plane. Spot two.

Stegosaurus had bony plates along its back to protect it from enemies. Find two.

Panoplosaurus was covered with knobs and spikes. Find five.

Anatosaurus had a kind of beak instead of a mouth. Spot three.

Corythosaurus had a hollow, bony plate on its head. Spot four.

Triceratops looked fierce, but it spent its time eating. Find two.

Dromaeosaurus stabbed its enemies with its sharp claws. Spot six.

Conifer forests

Black bears are good at climbing trees. Even the cubs can do it. Find four bears.

Snowshoe hares have furry feet to run in the deep snow in winter. Spot six hares.

Lynxes' beautiful coats blend with the shadows. Can you find three lynxes?

Spruce grouse only eat leaves and buds from spruce trees. Can you find four grouse?

Wolverines are also known as "gluttons". This means greedy people. Find three.

Skunks spray smelly liquid at their enemies. Find three.

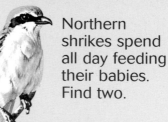

Forests cover the top of North America and Canada. The trees in them are mainly conifer trees that keep their leaves all year. Not many people live there, but lots of animals do. Can you spot 80 animals in this picture?

North American martens are fast and fierce hunters. Find three martens.

Chipmunks eat all summer, and sleep all winter. Find eight.

Northern shrikes spend all day feeding their babies. Find two.

Long-eared owls have two feathery tufts on their heads. Find four.

Beavers can cut down trees with their sharp teeth. Spot eight beavers.

Crossbills have hooked beaks to dig seeds out of fir cones. Find two.

Moose can wade through water with their long, thin legs. Find six moose.

Fishers attack porcupines. They bite their soft tummies. Spot four fishers.

Brown bears teach their cubs what to eat. Find two and a cub.

Flying squirrels can glide between trees. Spot five squirrels.

Mink slink along looking for voles and insects to eat. Can you find three mink?

Pumas are also called mountain lions or cougars. Spot three.

Ospreys swoop into water to catch fish. Find three.

Porcupines are covered in spikes called quills. Spot three.

Steamy swamps

Green tree frogs have suckers on their feet to climb slimy branches. Find eight frogs.

Otters can even eat fish while swimming on their backs. Spot six.

Snail kites only like eating one kind of snail. Can you find two snail kites?

Zebra butterfly. Spot four.

Fisher spiders eat insects clinging to the bottom of plant stems. Spot one.

Swamps are so wet you can't tell what is land and what is water. Many animals live in these watery worlds.

This picture shows part of a swamp in Florida, in the US, called the Everglades. Can you find 85 animals here?

Alligators. Spot six.

Gallinules are shy. They hide from enemies in the grass. Find four gallinules.

Gambusia fish eat mosquito eggs. There are plenty in the swamp. Find eight fish.

Bullfrog. Find three.

Bald eagles scoop fish up with their sharp claws. Find two.

Terrapins stick their skinny necks above water to take a look. Find ten.

Little blue herons wait for ages before spearing a fish. Spot two.

Raccoons use their front paws to scoop up fish and frogs from the water. Find six.

Cottonmouth snakes wiggle their bodies to swim along. Spot five.

Orb web spiders spin webs to catch passing insects. Find one.

Snapping turtles are experts at snapping up fish. Can you spot four turtles?

Anhingas dive underwater and stab fish with their beaks. Spot three.

Manatees swim slowly along, munching plants. Spot four.

Pileated woodpeckers keep their babies hidden. Spot three.

Garpike can easily tear up food with their sharp teeth. Spot three.

Dusty deserts

Coyotes often howl to each other to keep in touch. Can you find six?

Desert tortoises hide under the sand all day to stay cool. Spot four.

Burrowing owls move into empty burrows rather than dig them. Spot six.

Mexican red-kneed bird-eating spiders are poisonous, but only enough to kill an insect. Find six.

Trapdoor spiders crouch in tunnels and grab insects. Spot two.

Life is hard in the scorching deserts of North America. One part of them is so hot that it's called Death Valley. This picture shows part of the Sonoran Desert. If you look closely, you'll spot 95 animals that live in this dusty place.

Loggerhead shrikes push lizards onto cactus spikes. Spot four shrikes.

Black-tailed jackrabbits hop across the hot sand. Spot six jackrabbits.

Gila monsters lick insects' footprints to find them. Find four.

Gambel's quails blend in well with the desert. Can you find two?

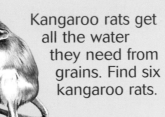

Kangaroo rats get all the water they need from grains. Find six kangaroo rats.

Crafty gila woodpeckers build nests inside cacti. Spot seven.

Rattlesnakes shake their tails to make a scary rattle. Find three rattlesnakes.

Elf owls often move into empty woodpeckers' nests. Find five.

American fringe-toed lizards dig in the sand with their noses and toes. Find eight.

Swallowtail butterfly. Find six.

Roadrunners run in zig-zags, to confuse enemies. Spot three more.

Kit foxes, or swift foxes, run very swiftly across the sand. Find three foxes.

Chuckwallas hide between rocks. Enemies can't see them. Can you spot three?

Peccaries can even eat cacti with their tough teeth. Find ten peccaries.

Musk oxen don't mind snow. Their thick coats keep them warm. Can you spot nine?

The Arctic

Thick fur keeps polar bears warm. Spot three and two cubs.

In the Arctic, winter is so cold that the sea freezes. Many animals go to warmer places until spring. This picture shows the Arctic at the end of a long, cold winter. There are 101 animals here for you to spot.

Humpback whales like this one visit the Arctic. They "sing" as they swim.

Lemmings live in cosy tunnels under the snow all winter. Find 11.

Stoats even squeeze into lemmings' tunnels. Find three stoats.

Baby seals have pale fur which drops out after a few weeks. Spot four.

Ptarmigans are white in winter and brown in summer. Can you find five?

Arctic ground squirrel. Find three.

Snowy owls hunt during the long Arctic day. Find three.

Raven.
Find
three.

Narwhals have
a horn sticking
out above their
mouths.
Spot two
narwhals.

Arctic foxes
bury animals
in the snow.
It's like a
freezer.
Find five.

Wolves often hunt
in a team called a
pack. Spot ten.

Orcas only kill fish
and seals for food.
Find two.

Walruses have
plenty of fat to
keep them warm.
Find 12.

Caribou dig
up plants under
the snow. Spot
11 caribou.

Five kinds of
seals live in
the Arctic.
Find one of
each kind.

Harp seal

Ribbon
seal

Hooded seal

Ringed seal

Bearded seal

White fur
disguises
Arctic hares
very well. Find
four others.

Beluga whale
babies turn white
when they are
two. Find a
mother and baby.

Under the sea

There are more than 20,000 kinds of fish in the world's rivers, lakes and seas. Some fish swim near the surface.

Others live in deep, dark water. This shows 22 kinds of sea creatures in the North Pacific Ocean.

These fishes' bodies light up in the gloomy deep water. Spot five of each kind.

Hatchet fish

Lantern fish

Fin whales swim along with their mouths open, swallowing food. Spot one.

Jellyfish sting smaller fish with their tentacles, then eat them. Find four jellyfish.

Angler fish wave a small fin above their mouths. Fish bite it and then get eaten. Find three.

Gulper eels can gulp down fish which are bigger than themselves. Find two eels.

If an octopus is being chased, it squirts out cloudy brown ink. Can you spot two?

Sponge

Sea lily

Sea spider

It is cold and dark at the bottom of the sea. Spot three of each of these creatures here.

78

Marlins' sharp noses can be dangerous for fishermen. Spot two.

Squid have ten arms with suckers on them to catch fish. Spot ten squid.

Huge basking sharks float near the surface of the sea. Can you spot one?

Dolphins often leap above the water. Nobody knows why. Spot four dolphins.

If skates feel threatened, they can give electric shocks. Find three.

Sea otters break open shells to eat the creatures inside. Find five otters.

Herring

Tuna

Sand eel

Groups of these fish swim near the surface. Spot a group of each.

Giant squid have big eyes to help them see in deep water. Find two.

Dall's porpoises swim fast. You can see their spray from far away. Find five.

Beard-worms. Can you spot a group?

Rainforests

Tapirs use their long noses to sniff for food among the bushes. Find three.

Emerald tree boas slither through the green trees. They are hard to spot. Find three.

Uakari monkey. Spot six.

Sloths move very slowly. They can spend their whole lives in one tree. Spot three.

Hummingbirds move their wings quickly and make a humming sound. Find three.

Hoatzins are strange birds. They smell awful. Spot two and a baby.

In rainforests, it rains almost every day. Trees and plants grow incredibly fast. This shows part of the Amazon Rainforest in Brazil. More kinds of animals and plants live here than anywhere else. Can you find 71 animals?

Toucans live in pairs. Their huge beaks are made of hollow bone. Spot four.

Black howler monkeys howl to each other to keep in touch. Spot four.

Silky anteaters look for ants. They lick them up with their long tongues. Find two.

Capybaras are good swimmers. They spend most of their time in the water. Spot ten.

Golden lion tamarins have manes of golden hair, like lions. Find three.

Golden cock-of-the-rock. Spot two.

Jaguars climb trees and swim across rivers to catch animals. Find one.

Anacondas can squeeze animals to death. Then they eat them whole. Find three.

Giant armadillos have thick, scaly skin to keep teeth and claws out. Spot two.

Amazon Indians use poison from arrow-poison frogs on the tips of their arrows. Find nine.

Blue and yellow macaw

Coral snakes are poisonous, so animals do not eat them. Spot three.

Spider monkeys are expert tree-climbers. Their tails help them hold on. Find three.

Many kinds of parrots live in the forest. Find one of each kind.

Hyacinth macaw

Golden conure

Scarlet macaw

Hot and dry

Fennec foxes even hear insects moving with their huge ears. Find four foxes.

Toad-headed agamid lizard. Spot four.

Desert hedgehogs try and keep out of the sun. Find four hedgehogs.

Mauritanian toad. Spot one.

Desert hares sit in the shade during the heat of the day. Find four hares.

Coursers can run fast to escape from enemies. Find four coursers.

Camels can last a week without water. Spot eight adults and a baby.

Deserts are the hottest, driest places on Earth, but many animals still manage to live in them. This picture shows part of the Sahara, the biggest desert in the world. Can you find 124 animals?

Sahara gecko. Spot one.

Jerboas hop across the sand like mini-kangaroos. Spot five.

Sand vipers bury themselves deep in the sand to stay cool. Find four vipers.

Desert centipede. Spot three.

Find one sandgrouse and her three chicks.

Darkling beetle. Spot three.

Skinks are hard to spot in the desert sand. Find four skinks.

Tiger beetles make a tasty snack for some animals. Spot three.

Little owl. Spot four.

Sand cats hunt smaller animals. Their fur blends in with the sand. Spot four cats.

Desert locusts. Find four.

Sidewinders slither along with an S-shaped wiggle. Find four sidewinders.

Scorpions sting animals with their poisonous tails. Spot three scorpions.

These animals don't mind the heat. They hardly need anything to drink.

Addax. Find five.

Barbary sheep. Spot 20.

Oryx. Spot ten.

Lanner falcon. Find two.

Sand rat. Spot three.

Dorcas gazelle. Spot eight.

Female elephants and babies live together. Male elephants live alone. Find seven.

Cheetahs run faster than any other animal, but they can't do it for long. Spot two.

Gerenuks can stand up on their back legs to reach the tastiest food. Spot two.

When vultures are flying, they can spot a meal a long way away. Spot nine vultures.

African plains

Ostriches are birds, but they can't fly. Find three ostriches and their nest.

Many of the world's best-known animals live in Africa, on huge, grassy plains. There are 17 kinds of animals here.

If you look closely, you can see what each kind eats. Most eat grass and leaves. Some kill other animals to eat.

Big groups of wildebeest wander across the plains looking for food. Find eight.

Rhinos attack enemies by charging at them, horn first. Spot three rhinos.

Baboon babies often ride on their parents' backs. Find eight baboons.

Hippos enjoy soaking in mud. It stops their skin from drying out. Find six.

Giraffes can reach food that no other animal can get to. Find four giraffes.

If a zebra sees an enemy, it barks to warn the others. Spot eight zebras.

Warthogs snuffle along, digging up food with their long tusks. Spot three warthogs.

Wild dogs roam the plains, searching for something to eat. Spot eight.

Thomson's gazelles jump and flash their white bottoms to confuse enemies. Spot ten.

Leopards often drag their food up into a tree to eat it in peace. Find two leopards.

Male lions look fierce, but lionesses do the most hunting. Spot six lions.

Lioness

Lion

Kori bustards are the heaviest flying birds on Earth. Can you find two bustards here?

Hidden homes

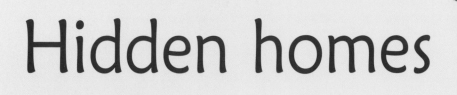

Spotted fallow deer are hard to see in the shadowy woods. Spot six deer.

Weasels often move into a home that another animal has left. Spot four weasels.

Magpies make messy nests and a lot of noise. Can you spot two magpies here?

Dormice sleep all winter. When they wake up, they start building a home. Spot five.

Woods like this are busy places in the spring. Many animals and birds are making homes for their babies. There are 18 different kinds of animals in this wood. Can you spot where each kind makes its home?

Wild boar babies are hard to see in the long grass in the woods. Can you spot eight boars?

When a shrew family goes out, each shrew holds on to the one in front. Spot ten.

Jays bury acorns in winter. In spring, they dig them up to eat. Spot four.

Woodpeckers grip trees with their claws while they eat insects. Find four.

Several rabbit families live together in one home. Spot nine rabbits.

Badgers only come out when it is getting dark. Can you spot four badgers?

Nightjars sit still all day. Their feathers blend well with the woods. Spot two.

Squirrels build one home for winter and another for summer. Spot four squirrels.

Tawny owls fly silently. They can catch animals without being heard. Spot three.

Both fox parents look after, and teach, their cubs. Can you spot five foxes?

Horseshoe bats only start coming out of their homes as darkness falls. Spot ten.

Stag beetles. Spot two.

Female   Male

If hedgehogs are scared, they roll up into a tough, spiny ball. Spot four hedgehogs.

By the sea

Most starfish have five arms. If one breaks off, they grow a new one. Spot five.

Rotting seaweed is a tasty meal for sandhoppers. Can you spot some sandhoppers?

Redshank use their long, thin beaks to find worms in the mud. Spot three.

Hermit crabs live in empty shells. As they grow, they move into bigger ones. Find four.

Spiny sea urchins push themselves along with their tough spikes. Spot three.

Crabs use their big claws to catch food. They can walk sideways, too. Spot six.

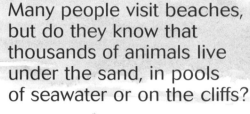

Many people visit beaches, but do they know that thousands of animals live under the sand, in pools of seawater or on the cliffs?

The sea covers this beach and goes out again, twice every day. When it is out, the beach looks like this. Can you spot 145 animals?

Puffin

Razorbill

Kittiwake

Guillemot

Many birds build their nests on the cliffs. Can you spot ten of each of these kinds?

 Acorn barnacles grow hard coats around themselves. Can you find some here?

 Lobsters are shy, but can give a nasty pinch with their big front claws. Spot two.

 Cormorants stand with their wings open, to dry their feathers. Find three.

 A snakelocks anemone simply splits in half to make two anemones. Find ten here.

 Prawns use their long feelers to search for tiny creatures to eat. Find ten prawns.

 On land, beadlet anemones look like blobs. In water, they look like this. Spot five.

Many seashore animals live in hard shells. Spot ten of each of these four kinds.

 Mussel   Limpet

 Common periwinkle

Dog whelk

Blennies hide in wet places while the sea is out. Spot six.

Oystercatchers knock shellfish off rocks with their sharp beaks. Can you spot six?

Mountains

Snow leopards, or ounces, hunt at night. They are harder to spot then. Find four.

Himalayan ibexes can clamber up slippery slopes to find food. Spot ten ibexes.

You can probably smell a takin before you see it. They smell oily. Spot two.

Male markhors spend the summer away from the females. Spot three males.

Bar-headed geese fly over the Himalayas each year. Can you spot ten geese?

Life is not easy high up in the mountains. It's cold and windy, and the ground is often covered with snow.

The 83 animals here live in the Himalayas, the highest mountains in the world. Can you spot them all?

Himalayan black bears live in forests on the mountain slopes. Find three bears.

Wallcreepers climb down slopes head first. Their claws help them grip. Spot four.

Apollo butterfly. Find three.

 If an animal dies, Himalayan griffon vultures swoop down and eat it. Spot six vultures.

 Pikas let plants dry in the sun, then store them to eat in winter. Find six pikas.

 Lammergeiers fly above the mountains, looking for dead animals to eat. Spot three.

Yaks have a coat of short fur, with long, shaggy hair on top to keep warm. Find five.

 Some people think a yeti, or "abominable snowman", made these footprints. Spot some.

 Male tahrs have thick fur and a collar of long hair around their heads. Spot three.

 While a group of bharals is eating, one keeps a look out for enemies. Spot two.

Alpine choughs push dead insects into cracks in rocks, to eat later. Spot ten choughs.

Marmots sleep in a burrow all winter. They block the door with grass to stay warm. Spot six.

Golden eagles are strong enough to carry off a baby deer. Spot two eagles.

Light and dark

Indian tailor-birds sew nests from leaves and grass. Spot three.

Tigers creep up behind animals. They leap on their backs and kill them. Find one.

Great Indian hornbills like this one use their big beaks to reach any hidden fruit.

Giant flying squirrels glide silently between the jungle trees. Can you spot one?

Gavials catch fish by sweeping their long jaws from side to side. Spot three.

Thick, hot rainforests are often called jungles. The story "Jungle Book" is set in a jungle like this one, in India. These pictures show the jungle by day and at night. Look at both of them and try to spot which of these animals come out during the day and which at night.

Indian elephants often march through the jungle in a line. Find four elephants.

Peacock

Male peacocks shake their tails to impress the female peahens. Find one of each.

Peahen

If muntjac deer are scared, they make loud barking noises, like a dog. Find two.

Slender lorises even walk on thin twigs, like this. Find one.

Leopards are expert tree-climbers and hunters. Find one leopard.

Dholes are wild dogs. They whistle to each other to stay in touch. Can you find four?

Pangolins curl up into a tight ball. Their scaly skin protects them. Find one.

Lazy sloth bears eat insects, fruit and even flowers. Can you spot a sloth bear?

Leopard cats look like mini-leopards. They are very shy. Can you spot one?

Madras tree shrews live hidden up in the trees, eating insects. Spot one.

Mongooses are brave. They even tease, and then kill, cobras. Spot one mongoose.

Gaurs are a kind of cow. If they are scared, they whistle. Spot two.

The poison from a king cobra's bite can kill a person in half an hour. Spot one.

Bonnet macaques get their name from the tufts of hair on their heads. Spot ten.

Magical world

If giant clams sense any danger, their huge shells shut tight. Find two giant clams.

Sea squirts. Find six.

Parrot fish use their hard lips to bite off lumps of coral to eat. Spot two parrot fish.

Sea cucumber. Spot two.

Stone fish lie on the seabed, looking like stones. Can you spot two?

Barracudas are fierce hunters, snapping up other fish. Spot three barracudas.

Bottlenose dolphins often leap over waves, following boats. Spot six dolphins.

When tiny sea creatures called corals die, their skeletons are left in the sea. Over thousands of years, millions of these build up to make a reef. The biggest reef in the world is the Great Barrier Reef, near Australia. Can you spot 125 animals and fish here?

Clown fish can hide in poisonous anemones. Find three clown fish somewhere.

Wrasses go into other fishes' mouths and clean their teeth. Spot two.

Snapper

Red emperor

Blue and gold angelfish

Blue damselfish

Goldman's sweetlips

Spot which fish doesn't belong in each of these five groups.

Sea sponge.
Find three.

Dugongs use their big top lip to pull plants from the seabed. Find three.

Sea horse babies grow in a pouch on their father's tummy. Spot six sea horses.

Lion fish. Find two.

Wobbegong sharks often lie still on the seabed, looking like shaggy rugs. Find one.

Bright flame shrimps nibble bugs off fishes' skins. Spot three shrimps.

Tiger cowrie. Spot three.

Manta rays flap through the water with their mouths open, catching food. Find two.

Blue sea star. Find two.

Can you guess how strange-looking hammerhead sharks got their name? Spot one.

There are many different kinds of coral. Can you find a clump of each of these four kinds?

Brain coral

Sea fan

Staghorn coral

Plate coral

Crown of thorns starfish eat coral. They can destroy whole reefs. Find four starfish.

Bright sea slugs slither across the coral. Spot three of each of these kinds of slug.

Naked sea slug

Sacoglossan sea slug

Spanish dancer

Out and about

Kangaroos use their big back legs to jump high up into the air. Spot ten.

Few animals risk attacking a thorny devil. Its spiky skin is too tough. Spot four.

Marsupial moles are always digging. They rarely come above ground. Find three.

Quolls have long noses for sniffing out food, and sharp teeth to eat it with. Spot two.

Shingle-backed skinks stick their blue tongues out at enemies. Spot two.

A lot of Australia is dry land, without many trees. People call it the outback. Not much rain falls, and it's very hot. Finding enough to eat and drink is tricky. There are 75 animals somewhere in this picture. Can you spot them?

Dingos are wild dogs. They live and hunt in a big group. Can you find six dingos?

Kookaburras sound as if they are laughing when they call to each other. Spot four.

Water-holding frogs soak up water like sponges. Spot three.

96

Mallee fowl lay their eggs in piles of leaves, covered with sand. Find two birds.

Frilled lizards have a fold of skin like a collar around their necks. Spot three.

Bandicoots often dig. Their babies snuggle in a safe pouch under their tummies. Spot two.

Goannas prefer to run away from their enemies than fight them. Spot three.

If echidnas are scared, they bury themselves. Only their spines show then. Spot three.

Hairy-nosed wombats live in underground burrows. Find three wombats.

Budgerigars or parakeets often fly around in a big flock. Find 20 budgerigars here.

Hopping mice usually run, but they can also hop fast on their back legs. Spot two.

Emus are fast runners, but they cannot fly at all. Can you spot three emus?

Emperor penguin chicks snuggle between their parents' feet. Spot a chick and five adults.

Antarctica

Sperm whales can stay underwater for an hour before coming up for air. Find one.

Antarctica is the coldest place on Earth. The sea is frozen nearly all year. Icy winds blow across the land.

It's hard to survive here, yet millions of birds and seals do. There are 195 animals and birds for you to find here.

Weddell seals can stay under the freezing water for an hour. Find five.

Rockhopper penguins are good at hopping on snow and rocks. Find 80.

Crabeater seals don't eat crabs. They eat tiny sea animals called krill. Find four.

Blue whales are easily the biggest animals on Earth. Can you spot one here?

Wandering albatrosses glide over the sea on their huge wings. Find one.

Macaroni penguins have feathers called crests on their heads. Spot nine.

 Blue-eyed shag. Spot three.

Gentoo penguins lay their eggs in nests made of stones. Spot 21 gentoo penguins.

Ross seals live on the solid ice away from other Antarctic animals. Find four.

Baby minke whales stay with their mothers for about a year. Spot a whale and her baby.

Chinstrap penguins sometimes lay their eggs on snow. Find 12 chinstraps.

Leopard seals catch penguins jumping into the sea. Spot five leopard seals.

Skuas fly over penguins' nests, waiting to kill their chicks. Find four skuas.

Adélie penguins leap from the sea onto the ice. Can you find 13?

Giant petrels eat so much they have to make themselves sick before taking off. Find four petrels.

King penguins lay one egg. Both parents guard it. Spot ten.

Male elephant seals fight to see who is stronger. Find ten elephant seals.

Fox

A closer look

Small white butterfly

Song thrush

Tips:

❀ Birds often come to a garden with a bird-table. They like eating cheese, seeds, fat and nuts.

❀ Lots of animals live in a pond. Others bathe in it, drink from it, or come to catch the animals in it.

❀ A "wild" patch of garden is a great place for insects to hide. Wild flowers might grow there, too.

❀ Berries on plants give birds a tasty meal. Plants that climb walls give them a nesting spot.

❀ Butterflies love bright flowers which smell beautiful. Try planting some in your garden.

❀ Flowerpots make a good home for some animals. Logs are handy for them to shelter under, too.

Animals don't only live in wild places. Lots live in gardens, like this one. There are 31 different kinds here.

Can you find two of each? On this page, there are ideas for things which may make more animals visit your garden.

Garden spider

Robin

Small tortoiseshell butterfly

Vole

Bumblebee

Blackbird

Snail

Earthworm

Wren

Dragonfly

Wood mouse

Woodlouse

Newt

Magpie

Red admiral butterfly

Hedgehog

Centipede

Greenfinch

Earwig

Frog

Slug

Chaffinch

Bullfinch

Peacock butterfly

Toad

Wasp

Mole

Millipede

On the farm

Baby turkeys are called poults. Find three turkey poults.

Farmers keep cows for their milk. A cow's baby is called a calf. Can you spot one?

Farmers train sheepdogs to help control sheep. Find three sheepdog puppies.

Shetland ponies are small but they are hard workers. Find a Shetland foal.

Rats often steal other animals' food. Some farmers poison them. Spot three baby rats.

Farmers keep goats for their milk. Baby goats are called kids. Spot two kids.

Farmers keep animals for their milk, meat, wool or eggs. Wild animals live on farms too. There are 19 kinds of animals in this picture. Each one has some babies hidden somewhere. Can you match the babies to the animals?

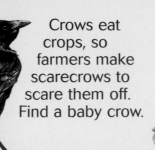

Crows eat crops, so farmers make scarecrows to scare them off. Find a baby crow.

Baby geese are called goslings. Feathers called down keep them warm. Find three.

Mice often build their nests in unusual places. Can you find four baby mice?

 Cats catch mice and rats. Find three baby cats, or kittens.

 Ducks swim on ponds. Find four baby ducks, or ducklings.

Bats sleep all day. Their babies eat at night. Spot two babies.

 Shire horses are a kind of large horse. Find a baby shire horse, or shire foal.

 Some chickens live inside, others roam outside. Can you spot three chicks?

 Pigs roll in muck, but like clean straw to sleep on. Find four baby pigs, or piglets.

 Donkeys can carry heavy loads. Can you spot a baby donkey, or foal?

Rabbits live in underground burrows. Can you spot three baby rabbits?

Barn owls hunt at night, swooping on mice and rats. Spot two owl chicks.

Baby sheep are called lambs. They are born in the spring. Find two lambs.

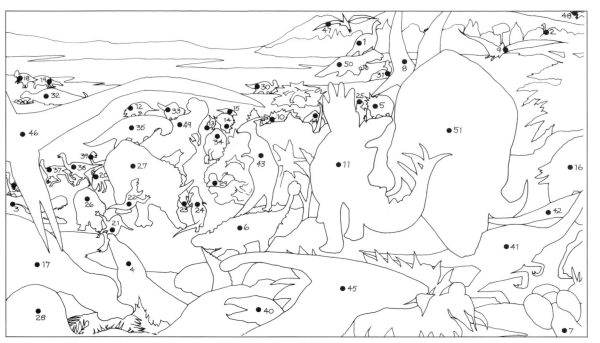

Back in time 68–69

Alamosaurus 1 2
Deinosuchus 3 4
Styracosaurus 5
Ankylosaurus 6 7
Quetzalcoatlus 8 9
Stegosaurus 10 11
Panoplosaurus 12 13
  14 15 16
Anatosaurus 17 18
  19
Dromaeosaurus 20
  21 22 23 24 25
Triceratops 26 27
Corythosaurus 28
  29 30 31
Maiasaura 32
Pachycephalosaurus
  33 34 35
Struthiomimus 36 37
  38 39 40 41 42
Parasaurolophus 43
  44 45
Pteranodon 46 47
  48
Tyrannosaurus 49
  50 51

Conifer forests 70–71

Skunks 1 2 3
Long-eared owls 4 5
  6 7
Beavers 8 9 10 11
  12 13 14 15
Crossbills 16 17
Moose 18 19 20 21
  22 23
Fishers 24 25 26 27
Brown bears 28 29
  30
Flying squirrels 31
  32 33 34 35
Mink 36 37 38
Porcupines 39 40
  41
Ospreys 42 43 44
Pumas 45 46 47
Northern shrikes 48
  49
Chipmunks 50 51
  52 53 54 55 56
  57
Martens 58 59 60
Wolverines 61 62 63
Spruce grouse 64
  65 66 67
Lynxes 68 69 70

Snowshoe hares 71
  72 73 74 75 76
Black bears 77 78
  79 80

Steamy swamps 72–73

Alligators 1 2 3 4 5
  6
Bald eagles 7 8
Terrapins 9 10 11 12
  13 14 15 16 17 18
Little blue herons
  19 20
Raccoons 21 22 23
  24 25 26
Cottonmouth snakes
  27 28 29 30 31
Orb web spider 32
Snapping turtles 33
  34 35 36
Garpikes 37 38 39
Pileated
woodpeckers 40 41
  42
Manatees 43 44 45
  46
Anhingas 47 48 49
Bullfrogs 50 51 52
Gambusia fish 53
  54 55 56 57 58
  59 60
Gallinules 61 62 63
  64
Fisher spider 65

Zebra butterfly 66
  67 68 69
Snail kites 70 71
Otters 72 73 74 75
  76 77
Green tree frogs 78
  79 80 81 82 83
  84 85

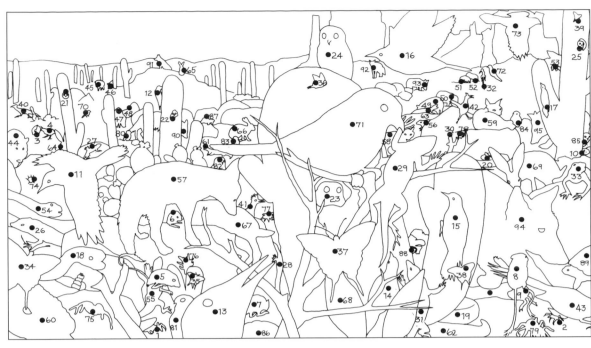

Dusty deserts 74–75

Trapdoor spiders 1 2

Gambel's quails 3 4

Kangaroo rats 5 6 7 8 9 10

Gila woodpeckers 11 12 13 14 15 16 17

Rattlesnakes 18 19 20

Elf owls 21 22 23 24 25

Fringe-toed lizards 26 27 28 29 30 31 32 33

Swallowtail butterflies 34 35 36 37 38 39

Roadrunners 40 41 42 43

Peccaries 44 45 46 47 48 49 50 51 52 53

Chuckwallas 54 55 56

Kit foxes 57 58 59

Gila monsters 60 61 62 63

Jackrabbits 64 65 66 67 68 69

Loggerhead shrikes 70 71 72 73

Mexican red-kneed bird-eating spiders 74 75 76 77 78 79

Burrowing owls 80 81 82 83 84 85

Desert tortoises 86 87 88 89

Coyotes 90 91 92 93 94 95

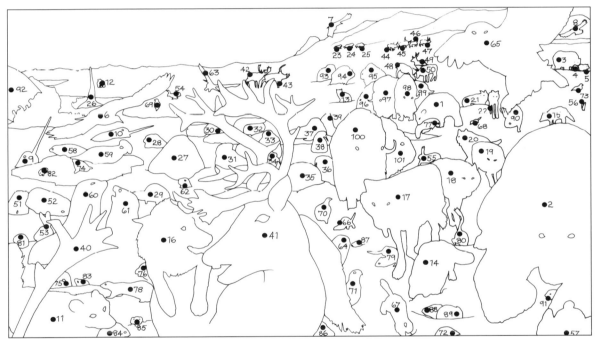

The Arctic 76–77

Polar bears 1 2 3 4 5

Ravens 6 7 8

Narwhals 9 10

Arctic foxes 11 12 13 14 15

Wolves 16 17 18 19 20 21 22 23 24 25

Killer whales 26 27

Walruses 28 29 30 31 32 33 34 35 36 37 38 39

Caribou 40 41 42 43 44 45 46 47 48 49 50

Beluga whales 51 52

Arctic hares 53 54 55 56 57

Ribbon seal 58

Hooded seal 59

Harp seal 60

Ringed seal 61

Bearded seal 62

Snowy owls 63 64 65

Arctic ground squirrels 66 67 68

Ptarmigans 69 70 71 72 73

Baby seals 74 75 76 77

Stoats 78 79 80

Lemmings 81 82 83 84 85 86 87 88 89 90 91

Humpback whale 92

Musk oxen 93 94 95 96 97 98 99 100 101

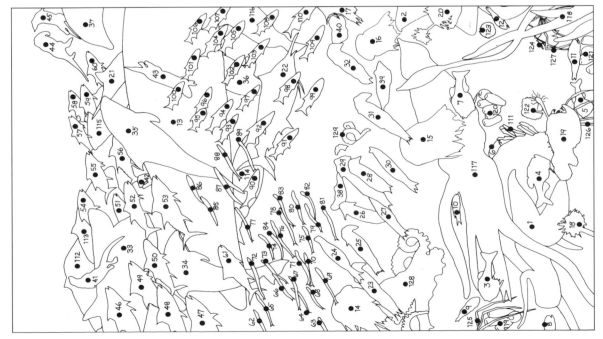

Under the sea 78–79

Gulper eels 1 2

Hatchet fish 3 4 5 6 7

Lantern fish 8 9 10 11 12

Fin whale 13

Jellyfish 14 15 16 17

Angler fish 18 19 20

Marlin 21 22

Squid 23 24 25 26 27 28 29 30 31 32

Basking shark 33

Dolphins 34 35 36 37

Skates 38 39 40

Sea otters 41 42 43 44 45

Tuna 46 47 48 49 50 51 52 53 54 55 56 57 58 59 60 61

Sand eels 62 63 64 65 66 67 68 69 70 71 72 73 74 75 76 77 78 79 80 81 82 83 84 85 86 87 88 89

Herring 90 91 92 93 94 95 96 97 98 99 100 101 102 103 104 105 106 107 108 109 110

Beardworms 111

Dall's porpoises 112 113 114 115 116

Giant squid 117 118

Sponges 119 120 121

Sea lilies 122 123 124

Sea spiders 125 126 127

Octopuses 128 129

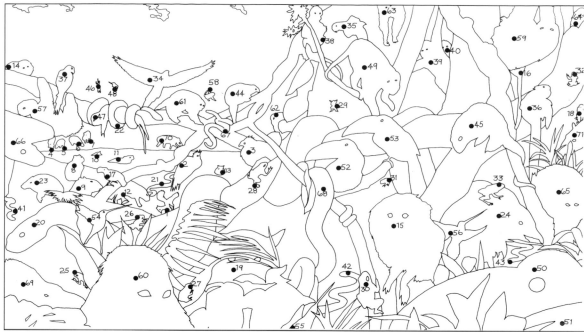

Rainforests 80–81

Hoatzins 1 2 3
Capybaras 4 5 6 7
  8 9 10 11 12 13
Golden lion tamarins
  14 15 16
Cocks-of-the-rock 17
  18
Jaguar 19
Anacondas 20 21
  22
Giant armadillos 23
  24
Arrow-poison frogs
  25 26 27 28 29
  30 31 32 33
Blue and yellow
  macaw 34
Scarlet macaw 35
Hyacinth macaw 36
Golden conure 37
Spider monkeys 38
  39 40
Coral snakes 41 42
  43
Silky anteaters 44
  45
Howler monkeys 46
  47 48 49

Toucans 50 51 52
  53
Hummingbirds 54
  55 56
Sloths 57 58 59
Uakari monkeys 60
  61 62 63 64 65
Emerald tree boas
  66 67 68
Tapirs 69 70 71

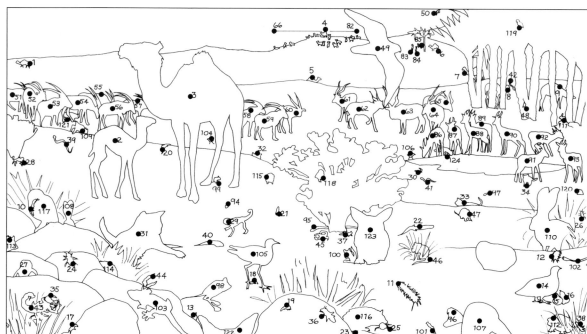

Hot and dry 82–83

Camels 1 2 3 4 5 6
  7 8 9
Desert centipedes
  10 11 12
Sandgrouse 13 14 15
  16
Darkling beetles 17
  18 19
Skinks 20 21 22 23
Tiger beetles 24 25
  26
Toad-headed lizards
  27 28 29 30
Sand cats 31 32 33
  34
Desert locusts 35 36
  37 38
Sidewinders 39 40
  41 42
Scorpions 43 44 45
Sand rats 46 47 48
Lanner falcons 49
  50
Oryxes 51 52 53 54
  55 56 57 58 59
  60
Addaxes 61 62 63
  64 65

Barbary sheep 66
  67 68 69 70 71
  72 73 74 75 76
  77 78 79 80 81
  82 83 84 85
Dorcas gazelles 86
  87 88 89 90 91
  92 93
Sand vipers 94 95
  96 97
Jerboas 98 99 100
  101 102
Sahara gecko 103
Coursers 104 105
  106 107
Desert hares 108
  109 110 111
Mauritanian toad 112
Desert hedgehogs
  113 114 115 116
Little owls 117 118
  119 120
Fennec foxes 121
  122 123 124

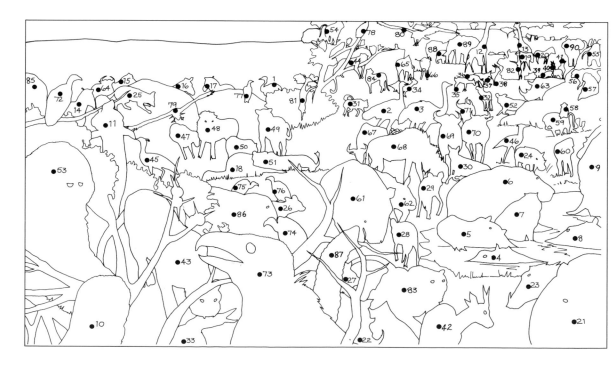

African plains 84–85

Ostriches 1 2 3
Hippos 4 5 6 7 8 9
Giraffes 10 11 12 13
Zebras 14 15 16 17
  18 19 20 21
Warthogs 22 23 24
Wild dogs 25 26 27
  28 29 30 31 32
Thomson's gazelles
  33 34 35 36 37
  38 39 40 41 42
Leopards 43 44
Kori bustards 45 46
Lions 47 48 49 50
  51 52
Baboons 53 54 55
  56 57 58 59 60
Rhinos 61 62 63
Wildebeest 64 65
  66 67 68 69 70
  71
Vultures 72 73 74
  75 76 77 78 79
  80
Gerenuks 81 82
Cheetahs 83 84
Elephants 85 86 87
  88 89 90 91

Hidden homes 86–87

Mole 1
Woodpeckers 2 3 4 5
Rabbits 6 7 8 9 10 11 12 13 14
Badgers 15 16 17 18
Nightjars 19 20
Squirrels 21 22 23 24
Tawny owls 25 26 27
Hedgehogs 28 29 30 31
Stag beetles 32 33
Horseshoe bats 34 35 36 37 38 39 40 41 42 43
Foxes 44 45 46 47 48
Jays 49 50 51 52
Shrews 53 54 55 56 57 58 59 60 61 62
Wild boars 63 64 65 66 67 68 69 70
Dormice 71 72 73 74 75
Magpies 76 77

Weasels 78 79 80 81
Fallow deer 82 83 84 85 86 87

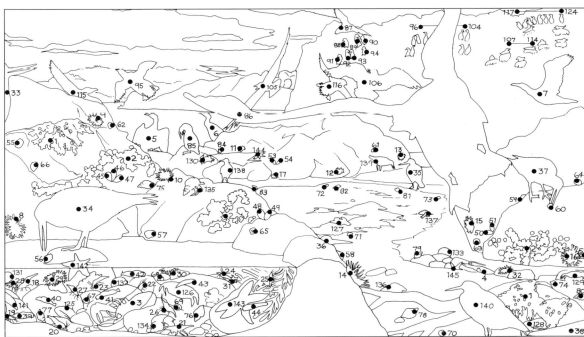

By the sea 88–89

Sandhoppers 1
Barnacles 2
Lobsters 3 4
Cormorants 5 6 7
Snakelocks anemones 8 9 10 11 12 13 14 15 16 17
Prawns 18 19 20 21 22 23 24 25 26 27
Beadlet anemones 28 29 30 31 32
Oystercatchers 33 34 35 36 37 38
Blennies 39 40 41 42 43 44
Mussels 45 46 47 48 49 50 51 52 53 54
Limpets 55 56 57 58 59 60 61 62 63 64
Periwinkles 65 66 67 68 69 70 71 72 73 74
Dog whelks 75 76 77 78 79 80 81 82 83 84

Puffins 85 86 87 88 89 90 91 92 93 94
Guillemots 95 96 97 98 99 100 101 102 103 104
Kittiwakes 105 106 107 108 109 110 111 112 113 114
Razorbills 115 116 117 118 119 120 121 122 123 124
Crabs 125 126 127 128 129 130
Sea urchins 131 132 133
Hermit crabs 134 135 136 137
Redshanks 138 139 140
Starfish 141 142 143 144 145

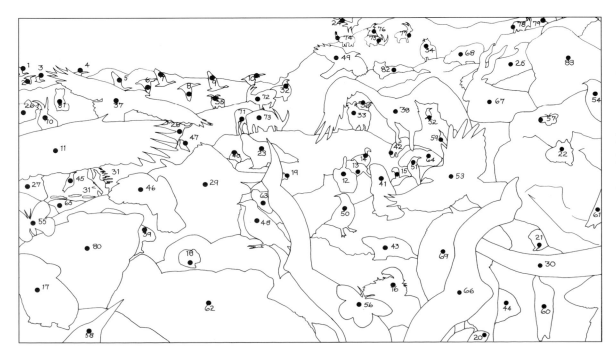

Mountains 90–91

Bar-headed geese 1 2 3 4 5 6 7 8 9 10
Griffon vultures 11 12 13 14 15 16
Pikas 17 18 19 20 21 22
Lammergeiers 23 24 25
Yaks 26 27 28 29 30
Yeti/abominable snowman footprints 31
Tahrs 32 33 34
Bharals 35 36
Golden eagles 37 38
Marmots 39 40 41 42 43 44
Alpine choughs 45 46 47 48 49 50 51 52 53 54
Apollo butterflies 55 56 57
Wallcreepers 58 59 60 61
Black bears 62 63 64

Markhors 65 66 67
Takins 68 69
Ibexes 70 71 72 73 74 75 76 77 78 79
Snow leopards 80 81 82 83

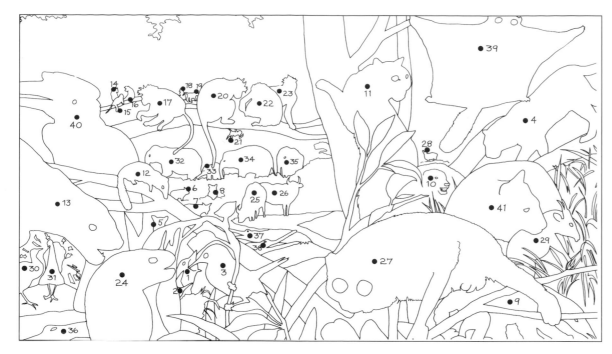

Light and dark 92–93

Tailor-birds 1 2 3
Leopard 4
Dholes 5 6 7 8
Pangolin 9
Sloth bear 10
Leopard cat 11
Madras tree shrew 12
Mongoose 13
Macaques 14 15 16 17 18 19 20 21 22 23
King cobra 24
Gaurs 25 26
Slender loris 27
Muntjac deer 28 29
Peacock/peahen 30 31
Elephants 32 33 34 35
Gavials 36 37 38
Giant flying squirrel 39
Hornbill 40
Tiger 41

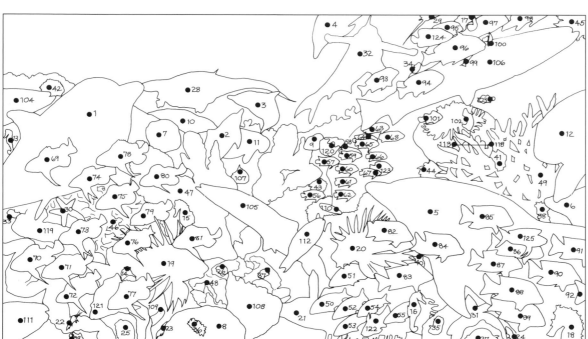

Magical world 94–95

Bottlenose dolphins 1 2 3 4 5 6
Sea sponges 7 8 9
Dugongs 10 11 12
Sea horses 13 14 15 16 17 18
Lion fish 19 20
Wobbegong 21
Flame shrimps 22 23 24
Tiger cowries 25 26 27
Manta rays 28 29
Blue sea stars 30 31
Hammerhead shark 32
Naked sea slugs 33 34 35
Sacoglossan sea slugs 36 37 38
Spanish dancers 39 40 41
Crown of thorns 42 43 44 45
Brain coral 46
Sea fan 47
Plate coral 48
Staghorn coral 49

Snappers 50 51 52 53 54 55
Angelfish 56 57 58 59 60 61 62 63 64 65 66 67 68
Damselfish 69 70 71 72 73 74 75 76 77 78 79 80 81
Red emperors 82 83 84 85 86 87 88 89 90 91 92
Sweetlips 93 94 95 96 97 98
Wrasses 99 100
Clown fish 101 102 103
Barracudas 104 105 106
Stone fish 107 108
Sea cucumber 109 110
Parrot fish 111 112
Sea squirts 113 114 115 116 117 118
Giant clams 119 120
"Odd" fish 121 122 123 124 125

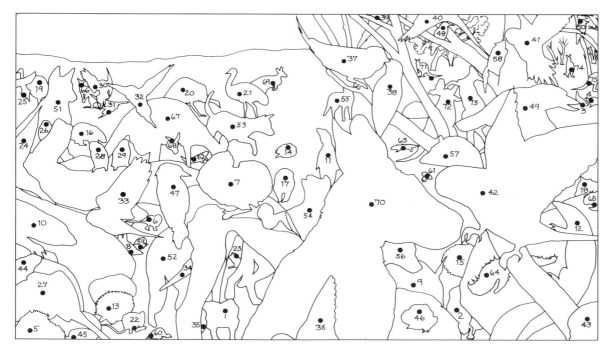

Out and about 96–97

Shingle-backed skinks 1 2
Mallee fowl 3 4
Frilled lizards 5 6 7
Bandicoots 8 9
Goannas 10 11 12
Echidnas 13 14 15
Wombats 16 17 18
Emus 19 20 21
Hopping mice 22 23
Budgerigars/parakeets 24 25 26 27 28 29 30 31 32 33 34 35 36 37 38 39 40 41 42 43
Water-holding frogs 44 45 46
Kookaburras 47 48 49 50
Dingos 51 52 53 54 55 56
Quolls 57 58
Marsupial moles 59 60 61
Thorny devils 62 63 64 65

Kangaroos 66 67 68 69 70 71 72 73 74 75

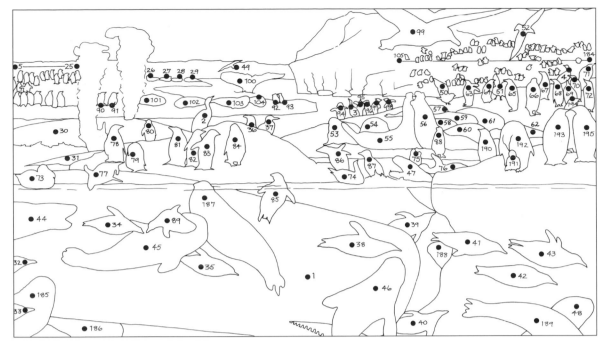

Antarctica 98–99

Sperm whale 1
Shags 2 3 4
Gentoo penguins 5 6 7
  8 9 10 11 12 13 14
  15 16 17 18 19 20
  21 22 23 24 25
Ross seals 26 27 28
  29
Minke whales 30 31
Chinstrap penguins
  32 33 34 35 36 37
  38 39 40 41 42 43
Leopard seals 44 45
  46 47 48
Skuas 49 50 51 52
Elephant seals 53 54
  55 56 57 58 59 60
  61 62
King penguins 63 64
  65 66 67 68 69 70
  71 72
Giant petrels 73 74 75
  76
Adélie penguins 77 78
  79 80 81 82 83 84
  85 86 87 88 89
Macaroni penguins 90
  91 92 93 94 95 96
  97 98

Albatross 99
Blue whale 100
Crabeater seals 101
  102 103 104
Rockhopper penguins
  105 106 107 108
  109 110 111 112 113
  114 115 116 117 118
  119 120 121 122 123
  124 125 126 127 128
  129 130 131 132 133
  134 135 136 137 138
  139 140 141 142 143
  144 145 146 147 148
  149 150 151 152 153
  154 155 156 157 158
  159 160 161 162
  163 164 165 166
  167 168 169 170
  171 172 173 174 175
  176 177 178 179 180
  181 182 183 184
Weddell seals 185 186
  187 188 189
Emperor penguins 190
  191 192 193 194
  195

A closer look 100–101

Foxes 1 2
Small white
butterflies 3 4
Song thrushes 5 6
Earthworms 7 8
Wrens 9 10
Dragonflies 11 12
Wood mice 13 14
Woodlice 15 16
Newts 17 18
Magpies 19 20
Red admiral
butterflies 21 22
Hedgehogs 23 24
Centipedes 25 26
Greenfinches 27 28
Earwigs 29 30
Frogs 31 32
Slugs 33 34
Chaffinches 35 36
Millipedes 37 38
Moles 39 40
Wasps 41 42
Toads 43 44
Peacock butterflies
  45 46
Bullfinches 47 48
Snails 49 50
Blackbirds 51 52

Bumblebees 53 54
Voles 55 56
Small tortoiseshell
butterflies 57 58
Robins 59 60
Garden spiders 61
  62

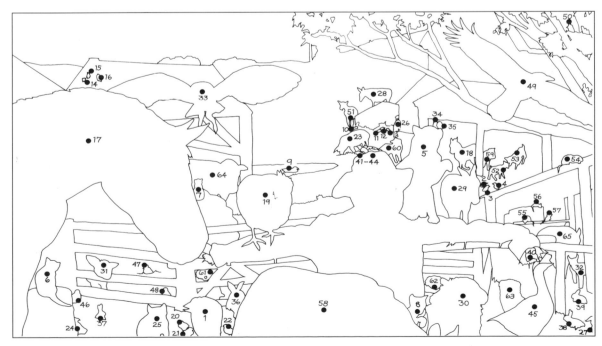

On the farm 102–103

Turkey 1
Turkey poults 2 3 4
Cat 5
Kittens 6 7 8
Duck 9
Ducklings 10 11 12
  13
Baby bats 14 15
Bat 16
Shire horse 17
Shire foal 18
Chicken 19
Chicks 20 21 22
Pig 23
Piglets 24 25 26 27
Donkey 28
Donkey foal 29
Sheep 30
Lambs 31 32
Barn owl 33
Owl chicks 34 35
Rabbit 36
Baby rabbits 37 38
  39
Mouse 40
Baby mice 41 42 43
  44
Goose 45
Goslings 46 47 48

Crow 49
Baby crow 50
Goat 51
Goat kids 52 53
Rat 54
Baby rats 55 56 57
Shetland pony 58
Shetland foal 59
Sheepdog 60
Puppies 61 62 63
Cow 64
Calf 65

109

Around the world

This is a map of the world. It shows you where all the places in this book are.

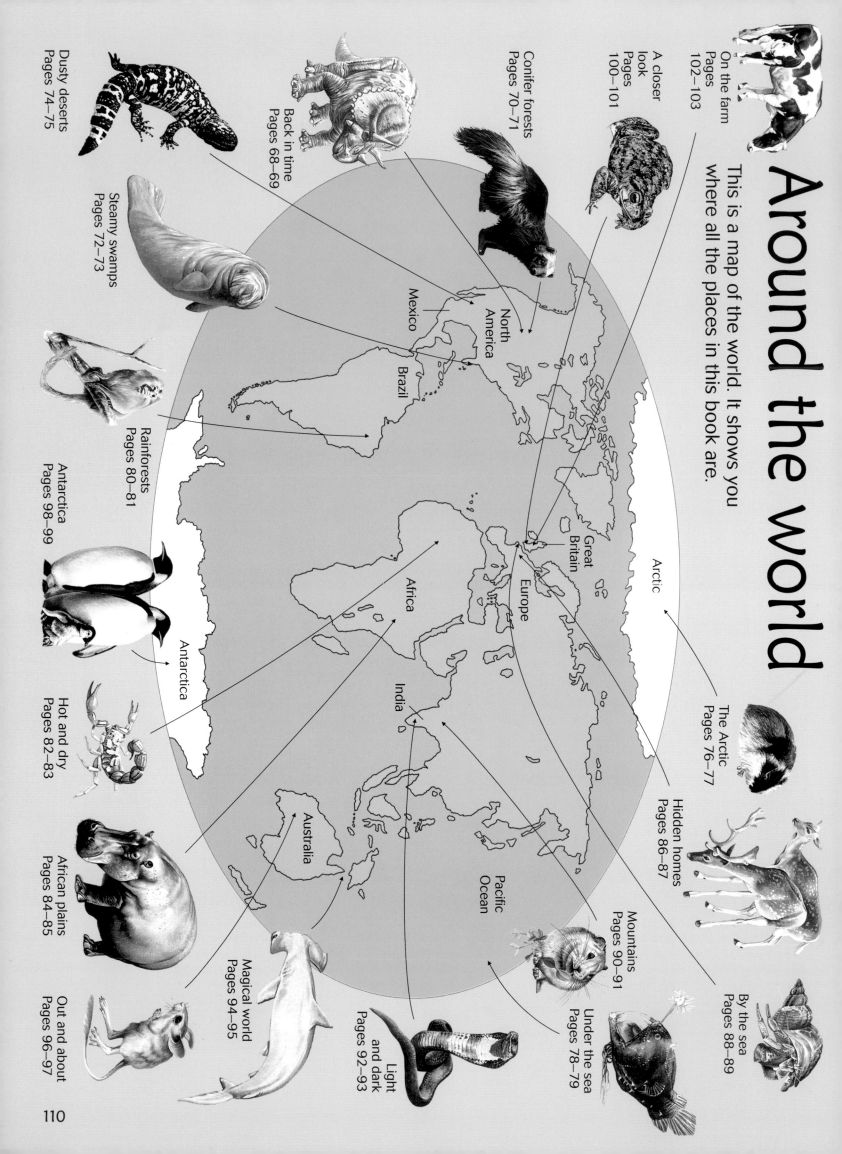

On the farm
Pages 102–103

A closer look
Pages 100–101

Conifer forests
Pages 70–71

Back in time
Pages 68–69

Steamy swamps
Pages 72–73

Dusty deserts
Pages 74–75

Rainforests
Pages 80–81

Antarctica
Pages 98–99

Hot and dry
Pages 82–83

African plains
Pages 84–85

Out and about
Pages 96–97

Magical world
Pages 94–95

Light and dark
Pages 92–93

Under the sea
Pages 78–79

Mountains
Pages 90–91

By the sea
Pages 88–89

Hidden homes
Pages 86–87

The Arctic
Pages 76–77

Mexico

North America

Brazil

Great Britain

Europe

Arctic

Africa

Antarctica

India

Australia

Pacific Ocean

Index

abalones 21
airbags 23
air gauge 19
albatrosses 98
alligators 72
ammonites 4, 9
anchors 6
anemones
    beadlet 8; deep sea 17;
    poisonous 19
anhingas 73
anteaters 80
antelopes
    addaxes 83
    oryxes 83
ant-lions 38, 70
ants
    bulldog 44, 76; harvester
    38, 70; honey 39, 71;
    leafcutter 43, 75; weaver
    53, 85; wood 48, 80
archelon 4
armadillos 81
astrolabes 13

baboons 84
backswimmers 46
badgers 87
bandicoots 97
barnacles 9, 89
barrels 12
baskets 13, 23
bathyscaphes 16
bats 87, 103
BC (Buoyancy Control)
    jackets 19
beardworms 16, 79
bears
    black 70; brown 71;
    Himalayan black 90; polar
    67, 76; sloth 93
beavers 71
bees
    bumblebees 48; honeybees
    37, 57;
beetles
    bark 49; blister 39; burying
    49; cockchafer 52; darkling
    83; Devil's coach-horses 37;
    great diving 47; ground 55;
    harlequin 43; Hercules 38,
    43; histerid 55; jewel 53;
    leaf 42; longhorn 41, 49,
    54; longicorn 52;
    rhinoceros 54; stag 48, 87;
    tiger 83; whirligig 47;
belemnites 5
bharals 91
bikes 6
birds
    albatrosses 27; Arctic skuas
    11; Arctic terns 11;
    boobies 15, 27; cormorants
    26; frigate birds 14, 26;
    glossy ibis 24; kingfishers
    25; kittiwakes 8; little auks
    11; ospreys 24;
    oystercatchers 9; pelicans
    26; penguins 27; puffins 11;
    swallow-tailed gulls 26
black smokers 17
blackbirds 100

blennies 89
budgerigars/parakeets 97
bugs 43
    assassin 42, 54; bark 43;
    giant water 51; lantern 53;
    rosea 41; shield 41, 45, 53;
    spittle 37; stilt 43;
    thornbugs 42
bullfinches 101
buoys 19
butterflies 41
    Apollo 90; birdwing 53;
    common blue 37; common
    grass yellow 45; Hamadryas
    42; monarch 45, 55;
    morpho 43; peacock 101;
    purple emperor 49; red
    admiral 101; small
    tortoiseshell 100; small
    white 100; swallowtail 54,
    75; viceroy 51; zebra 51, 72

caddisflies 46, 47
cameras 13, 18
cannonballs 13
cannons 13
capybaras 81
caribou 67, 77
caterpillars
    cinnabar moth 36; emperor
    gum moth 45; hawk moth
    42; processionary moth; 44,
    55; swallowtail butterfly 54
cats 103
centipedes 37, 83, 101
    red 52
chaffinches 101
chamas 24
cheetahs 67, 20
chests of coins 12
chickens 103
chipmunks 70
choughs 91
chuckwallas 75
cicadas 53
clams 18
    giant clams 94
cockchafers 52
cockroaches 36
    hissing 41
cocks-of-the-rock 81
cone shells 18
consoles 19
coral 6, 19, 94, 95
cormorants 89
cougars/mountain lions/pumas
    71
coursers 82
cowries 95
cows 102
coyotes 74
crabs, 88
    blue land 51; deep sea 17;
    edible 9; fiddler 25, 50;
    hermit 8; kelp 20; king 5;
    Sally lightfoot 27;   shore
    9; soldier 24; velvet
    swimming 9
crane flies 48
crickets 54
crocodiles 24
crossbills 71

crown
of
thorns 95
crows 102

daggers 12
damselflies 46
deer
    fallow 86; muntjac 92
depth gauge 19
Devil's coach-horses 37
dholes 93
dingos 96
dinosaurs 67, 68, 69
divers
    cutting 22; exploring wreck
    7; in cage 14; measuring 13;
    sketching 12
divers' signals 18
dividers 13
diving bells 22, 23
dog whelks 89
    dolphins 26, 14, 79, 94
    common 26; spinner
    14; spotted 26
donkeys 103
dormice 86
dragonflies 35, 40, 47, 101
    darter 48; emperor 40;
    green darner 51
ducks 103
dugongs 95

eagles 67, 73, 91
earthworms 101
earwigs 37, 101
echidnas 97
eels
    conger 22; gulper 17;
    moray 7
elasmosaurus 4
elephants
    African 84; Indian 92
empid flies 48
emus 97

falcons 83
fins 18
fireflies 52
fish
    angelfish 7, 94; angler fish
    16, 78; anthias 7; banjo fish
    4; barracudas 19, 94;
    basking sharks 79;
    blacksmith 21; blennies 9;
    butterfish 8; butterfly fish 7;
    cleaner fish 7; clown fish
    19, 94; clown triggerfish
    19; cod 23; crocodile fish
    6; damselfish 94; flying fish
    14; gambusia fish 72;
    garpikes 73; glass fish 7;
    gobies 8; groupers 7;
    gulper eels 78; halfmoons
    21; hammerhead sharks 95;
    hatchet fish 16, 78; herring
    79; kelpfish 21; lantern fish
    17, 78; lion fish 7, 95; manta
    rays 95; marlins 14, 79;
    moorish idols 19;
    mudskippers 24; ocean

    goldfish 20;
    opaleyes 21;
    parrot fish 6;
    pollack 23; puffer fish
    7; rabbit fish 4; red
    emperors 94; remoras 14;
    sailfish 15; sand-eels 79;
    senoritas 21; skates 79;
    snappers 94; stone fish 94;
    surgeon fish 19; sweetlips
    94; tripletail fish 25; tripod
    fish 16; tuna 15, 79; vent
    fish 17; viper fish 17;
    wrasses 6, 21, 94
    (see also eels, rays and
    sharks)
fishermen 15
fishers 71
flashlights 7
flatworms 40
fleas 36
foxes 87, 100
    fennec 82; kit/swift 75
frogs 25, 101
    arrow-poison 81; bullfrogs
    72; green tree 72; water-
    holding 96

gallinules 72
gaurs 93
gavials 92
gazelles 83, 85
geckos 82
geese 90, 102
geosaurus 5
gerenuks 84
giant red velvet mites 39
gila monsters 74
giraffes 85
goannas 97
goats 102
    ibexes 90
gold bars/ingots 6, 13
gold cups 12
gold plates 12
grasshoppers 42, 43
    lubber 51; painted 38
greenfinches 101
greenflies 37
grouse 70, 83
guillemots 88

hand blowers 12
hares
    Arctic 77; desert 82;
    snowshoe 70
hardsuits 22
hedgehogs 82, 87, 101
helmets 22
herons 73
hippos 85
hoatzins 80
hornbills 92
hornets 49
horseflies 49
horses, shire 103
houseflies 36
hummingbirds 80

ichthyosaurus 4
ingots 13

jackrabbits 74
jaguars 81
jars 12
jays 86
jellyfish 4, 18, 78
jerboas 82
jewels 13

kangaroos 96
kelp holdfasts 21
kites, snail 72
kittiwakes 88
knives 19
kookaburras 96
kori bustards 85

lammergeiers 91
lampshells 5
larvae 35
    ant-lion 38; caddisfly 47;
    great diving beetle 47;
    honeybee 57; midge 51;
    mosquito 46; sawfly 44;
    termite 56
lemmings 76
leopard cats 93
leopards 85, 93
lifting bags 13
limpets 8, 89
lions 85
lizards 75, 83, 97
lobsters 89
locusts 55, 83
lorises 92
lynxes 70

macaques 25
macaws/parrots 81
magpies 86, 101
mallee fowl 97
manatees 9
mangrove seedlings 25
manipulator arms 17
marine iguanas 27
markhors 90
marmots 91
martens 70
masks 18
mayflies 47
metal detectors 12
mice 97, 101, 102
midges 51
millipedes 101
    flat-backed 53; giant 40; pill
    41
mink 71
monkeys
    howler 80; macaques 93;
    tamarins 81; uakari 80
moles 86, 96, 101
mongooses 93
moose 71
mosquitoes 46, 50
moths
    African moon 55; Atlas 52;
    bogong 45; cinnabar 36;
    emperor gum 44; io 50;
    loepa 52; poplar hawk 49;
    processionary 55; yucca 39
mountain lions/cougars/pumas
    71
musk oxen 76
muskets 12
mussels 8, 23, 89

narwhals 11, 77
nets
    purse seine 14; shrimping
    net 9

newts 101
nightjars 87
nymphs 35
    dragonfly 35, 47; praying
    mantis 41; shield bug 41

octopuses 9, 21, 67, 78
ospreys 71
ostriches 84
otters 20, 24, 72, 79
otters 20, 24
ounces/snow leopards
    66, 90
owls
    barn 103; burrowing 74; elf
    75; little 82; long-eared 71;
    snowy 76; tawny 87
oysters 24
oystercatchers 89

pangolins 93
parakeets/budgerigars 97
parrots/macaws 81
peacocks 92
peahens 92
peccaries 75
penguins 27
    Adélie 99; chinstrap 99;
    emperor 98; gentoo 99;
    king 99; macaroni 98;
    rockhopper 98
periwinkles 89
petrels 99
pigs 66, 103
pikas 91
placodus 4
plesiosaurus 5
pliosaurus 5
polar bears 10
ponies, Shetland 102
porcupines 71
porpoises 79
Portuguese men-of-war 15
prawns 9, 89
praying mantids 41, 55
proboscis monkeys 25
ptarmigans 66
pterosaurs/"flying lizards"
    Pteranodon 68;
    Quetzalcoatlus 69
puffins 88
pumas/cougars/
    mountain lions 71

quails 75
quolls 96

rabbits 87, 103
raccoons 73
rats 75, 83, 102
ravens 77
rays
    bat 20; manta 14
razorbills 88
redshank 88
regulators 18
rhinos 84
rigs 22
roadrunners 75
robins 100
ROVs (Remotely Operated
    Vehicles) 17, 23

sand cats 83
sandhoppers 88
sawflies 44
scorpions 39, 83
    water 47; whip 38
sea anemones 89

sea cucumbers 5, 94
sea fans 95
sea horses 95
sea lilies 4, 78
sea slugs 18, 95
sea snails 20
sea spiders 78
sea squirts 94
sea snakes:
    black and yellow 14; dog-
    headed 24; olive 18
sea spiders 16
sea stars 20, 95
sea urchins 5, 21, 88
sea wasps 18
seals
    bearded 77; crabeater 98;
    elephant 99; harp 77;
    hooded 77; leopard 99;
    ribbon 77; ringed 77; Ross
    99; Weddell 98
sealions
    Californian 20; Galápagos
    26
seals
    baby 10; bearded 10;
    Galápagos fur 27; grey 8,
    23; harp 11; ribbon 11;
    ringed 11
shags 99
sharks:
    basking 79; great white
    15; hammerhead 6, 95;
    prehistoric 5; reef 6; tiger
    27; whale 15
sheep 83, 103
sheepdogs 102
ships
    diving support vessel 23;
    kelp harvesting ship 21;
    pipe-laying barge 22;
    research ship 10
shrews 86
shrikes 70, 74
shrimps 66, 95
silver ingots 13
skinks 66, 83, 96
skuas 99
skunks 67, 70
sloths 67, 80
slugs 49, 101
snails 36, 52, 100
    African land 54; apple 50;
    hedge 48; pond 47; tree 51
snakes
    anacondas 81; coral snakes
    81; cottonmouth snakes 73;
    emerald tree boas 80; king
    cobras 93; rattlesnakes 75;
    sand vipers 82; sidewinders
    83
snorkels 18
sonar "fish" 16
snow leopards/ounces
    66, 90
song thrushes 100
spiders
    bird-eating 67, 74; black
    widow 39; crab 49; fisher 46,
    51; fisher spiders 72; garden
    spiders 36, 100; gliding 45;
    golden orb weaver 50; hairy
    bird-eating 52; jumping 50;
    lynx 38, 41; Mexican red-
    kneed Nephila 53; net
    throwing 45; orb web spiders
    9; redback 44; red-kneed
    bird-eating 38; Sydney
    funnel-web 44; tarantulas 39;

thorn 40; trapdoor spiders
    39, 74; wandering 42; zebra
    37
sponges 5, 78, 95
squat lobsters 9
squid 17, 26, 79
squirrels 66, 71, 87, 92
stalk-eyed flies 55
starfish 5, 8, 66, 88, 95
stick insects 40
    giant 44; water 47
stoats 76
stoneflies 46
submarines 10
submersibles 16, 17
sundials 13
swords 12

tahrs 91
tailor-birds 92
takins 90
tanks 18
tanystropheus 5
tapirs 80
termites 53, 56
terrapins 73
thorny devils 96
tigers 66, 92
toads 82, 101
tortoises 74
toucans 80
transmitters 10
tree shrews 93
tsetse flies 54
turtles 4, 15, 25, 73

umbilicals 23

voles 100
vultures 84, 91

wallcreepers 90
walruses 10, 77
warthogs 85
wasps 37, 101
    potter 54; tarantula hawk
    39
water jet pumps 23
water striders 46
weasels 86
weevils
    giraffe-necked 40; hairy 41
weights 19
wetsuits 19
whales
    beluga 10, 77; blue 11, 66,
    98; fin 78; gray 20;
    humpback 11, 76; killer 11;
    minke 99; narwhal 11, 77;
    pilot 27;orca 77; sperm 17, 98
whistles 13
wild boars 86
wild dogs 85
wildebeest 84
witchetty grubs 45
wobbegongs 95
wolverines 70
wolves 77
wombats 97
woodlice 101
woodpeckers 73, 75, 87
wrens 101

yaks 91
yetis/abominable
    snowmen 91

zebras 85